Exploring
EARTH AND SPACE SCIENCE

1

ACI–CAL

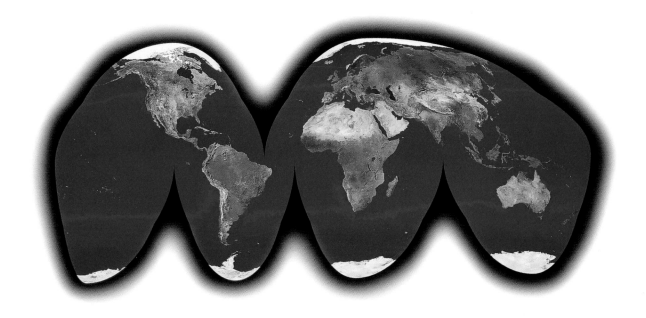

Marshall Cavendish
New York • London • Toronto • Sydney

Marshall Cavendish Corporation
99 White Plains Road
Tarrytown, New York 10591

Website: www.marshallcavendish.com

© 2002 Marshall Cavendish Corporation

Created by **Brown Partworks Limited**

Library of Congress Cataloging-in-Publication Data

Exploring earth and space science.
     p. cm.
    Includes bibliographical references and indexes.
    Contents: 1. Acid and base-Calcium -- 2. Calendar-Continental shelf -- 3. Copper-El
Niño and La Niña -- 4. Energy-Gondwana -- 5. Grassland-Laser -- 6. Light-Meteor -- 7.
Meteorology-Ordovician period -- 8. Ore-Prospecting -- 9. Protein-Star -- 10.
Stratosphere-X ray -- 11. Index.
    ISBN 0-7614-7219-3 (set) -- ISBN 0-7614-7220-7 (v. 1) -- ISBN 0-7614-7221-5 (v. 2)
-- ISBN 0-7614-7222-3 (v. 3) -- ISBN 0-7614-7223-1 (v. 4) -- ISBN 0-7614-7224-X (v.
5) -- ISBN 0-7614-7225-8 (v. 6) -- ISBN 0-7614-7226-6 (v. 7) -- ISBN 0-7614-7227-4
(v. 8) -- ISBN 0-7614-7228-2 (v. 9) -- ISBN 0-7614-7229-0 (v. 10) -- ISBN
0-7614-7230-4 (v. 11)
    1. Earth sciences--Encyclopedias. 2. Space sciences--Encyclopedias. 3.
Astronomy--Encyclopedias

QE5 .E96 2002

550'.3--dc21
        00-065801
        CIP
        AC

ISBN 0-7614-7219-3 (set)
ISBN 0-7614-7220-7 (vol. 1)

Printed in Hong Kong

06 05 04 03 02 01 00   5 4 3 2 1

PHOTOGRAPHIC CREDITS

Corbis: *14,* Natalie Fobes *70,* Charles E. Rotkin *50,* Jeffery L. Rotman *49,* World Panoramas *74–75*
DCC (Navy): *18* Ministry of Defence
Mary Evans Picture Library: *55*
NASA: *35, 37, 38, 39, 66*
NSSDC photo gallery: *51*
NOAA: Dr. Yohsuke Kamide *58/59,* Giuseppe Zibordi *32/33*
Science Photo Library: *25, 67, 71, 72,* W. Bacon *62,* Martin Bond *54,* Crown Copyright/Health
Safety Laboratory *12/13,* Ken Eward *56/57,* Simon Fraser *40,* David A. Hardy *45,* Lizzie Harper *27,*
Harvard College Observatory *47,* Laguna Design *26,* Max Planck Institute für Extraterrestrische
Physik *44–45,* David Nunuk *31, 46,* Sam Ogden *23,* Alfred Pasieka *68,* Philippe Plailly *73,* Prof. P.
Motta *78,* John Reader *22,* Volker Steger *29,* Takeshi Takahara *17,* Tek Image *28,* Tom Van Sant,
Geosphere Project/Planetary Visions *48,* Joe Tucciarone *43,* David Vaughn *34,* Charles D. Winters *10*
Trip: CC *60,* S. Grant *65,* P. Kerry *52–53,* H. Rogers *30,* D. Saunders *19,* C. Smedley *16,* Th-Foto
Werbung *15*

Front cover: Montage of the planet Neptune behind Triton, one of its moons (NASA)

Title page: Projection of Earth's land and oceans (Science Photo Library, Worldsat
        International and J. Knighton)

Back cover: How a mirage occurs (Marshall Cavendish)

How to Use This Set

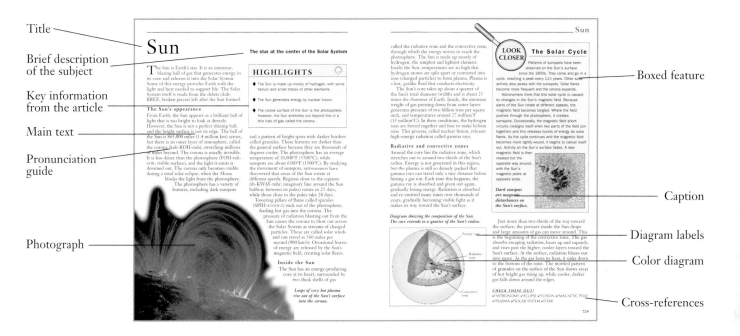

Title

Brief description of the subject

Key information from the article

Main text

Pronunciation guide

Photograph

Boxed feature

Caption

Diagram labels

Color diagram

Cross-references

This page explains how to use the 11 volumes of *Exploring Earth and Space Science*.

There are more than 300 articles arranged alphabetically in volumes 1 to 10. The articles cover earth science, space science, the environment, chemistry, and physics. Each volume has its own glossary, which explains terms that appear in the articles, and an index, which will help you find references to particular subjects in that volume.

Volume 11 contains a range of information, from time lines of Earth's history and the history of science to places to go and things to do. You will also find a complete glossary and comprehensive index in volume 11.

Every article is illustrated with photographs or labeled diagrams and has the following features: a title, a brief definition of the subject, a pronunciation guide for difficult or unusual words, a HIGHLIGHTS box that lists key information from the entry, and a CHECK THESE OUT! section, which guides you to related articles in the set.

Other boxed features also appear in many articles to provide more detailed information about topics of particular interst. For example:

◆ LOOK CLOSER—an in-depth discussion about a point covered in the main text. For example, in the entry Jupiter the Look Closer box tells you about Jupiter's family of 16 moons.

◆ DISCOVERERS—these boxes describe scientists who have made important discoveries in their field, such as the physicist Marie Curie, who is described in the entry Radioactivity.

◆ STORY OF SCIENCE—memorable events from the history of science are told in these boxes. Turn to the entry Optics, for example, to find out how Isaac Newton invented the reflecting telescope.

◆ THE FUTURE—the scientific advances that might change our lives in the future. In Fiber Optics, for example, you can find out how computers might one day use pulses of light to transmit data, making them run thousands of times faster.

◆ EVERYDAY SCIENCE—how physical sciences are put to use in technology, industry, and everyday life. In the entry Gas, for example, you can find out how the noble gas neon is used to make colorful neon lights.

Contents

Contents by Area of Interest

Use the following list of articles to find subjects of special interest to you. The articles in this encyclopedia fall into five general categories. Some article titles appear in more than one category. Volume numbers appear in **boldface type** followed by colons and the number of the first page of each article.

- SPACE SCIENCE
- EARTH SCIENCE
- ENVIRONMENT
- CHEMISTRY
- PHYSICS

ENVIRONMENT

CHEMISTRY

Contents by Area of Interest

PHYSICS

Acid and Base

**Families of compounds that
can neutralize each other**

In everyday life, there are many common acids and bases. Citrus fruits have a sharp flavor because they contain citric acid. Hydrochloric acid in the stomach aids digestion (food breakdown) by attacking food, while the formic acid secreted by some ants causes uncomfortable bites that are actually chemical burns. Ammonia is a base that dissolves in water. It is included in household cleaning products, as it attacks dirt.

In 1884, Swedish chemist Svante Arrhenius (1859–1927) defined an acid as a substance that forms hydrogen ions (H^+) when it dissolves in water, and a base as a substance that produces hydroxide ions (OH^-) when dissolved in water. This definition fits with

Vinegar (acetic acid) being added to washing soda (sodium carbonate, a base). The result will be a salt (sodium acetate), water, and carbon dioxide.

the observation that water is produced in a neutralization reaction, since hydrogen ions react with hydroxide ions to form water. The Arrhenius definition is assumed by most chemists when talking about acids and bases acting in aqueous (water-based) solutions.

Early studies of acids and bases

In the 18th century, French chemists Antoine (1743–1794) and Marie (1758–1836) Lavoisier noticed that certain corrosive (having the ability to wear away) substances released bubbles of a gas when they attacked metals such as zinc. When they burned this gas, they observed that the vapors rising from the flame formed water when they condensed on a cold surface. They called this gas hydrogen and gave the name *acid* to a substance that could produce hydrogen in this way.

The Lavoisiers noticed that certain substances made acids incapable of attacking metals. They classed these substances as bases. The reaction between an acid and a base is called a neutralization reaction. An example is the reaction between sulfuric acid and sodium hydroxide. A neutralization reaction produces a salt (in this case, sodium sulfate) and water:

$$H_2SO_4 + 2NaOH \rightarrow Na_2SO_4 + 2H_2O.$$

Hydrogen ions in solution

When hydrogen chloride gas (HCl) dissolves in water, it forms a solution of hydrochloric acid. The solution contains chloride ions (Cl^-) and hydrogen ions (H⁺). The hydrogen ions do not float freely in water. They attach themselves to water molecules to form hydronium ions (H_3O^+). This happens because a hydrogen ion, a proton , attaches itself to a pair of electrons on the oxygen atom of a water molecule.

In a similar way, when ammonia (NH_3) dissolves in water, the nitrogen atom in ammonia has a pair of electrons that attracts hydrogen ions more strongly than the oxygen pair does, so it forms the ammonium ion (NH_4^+). The water molecules that give up hydrogen ions become hydroxide ions. When hydrochloric acid and ammonia solution react together, they form the salt ammonium chloride (NH_4Cl) and water.

Nonaqueous solutions

When hydrogen chloride dissolves in pure liquid ammonia, it forms ammonium chloride only. Liquid ammonia contains no hydroxide ions, so water does not form. In 1923, Danish chemist Johannes Brønsted (1879–1947) and British chemist Thomas Lowry (1874–1936) worked independently to create a new definition to include such reactions. In the Brønsted-Lowry theory, an acid is a proton donor (in this case, hydrogen chloride) and a base is a proton acceptor (in this case, ammonia).

Also in the 1920s, U.S. chemist Gilbert Newton Lewis (1875–1946) developed the definition of acids and bases by classing bases as electron donors and acids as electron acceptors. In the case of the reaction between hydrogen chloride and ammonia, for example, the hydrogen ion accepts electrons when it attaches itself to an ammonia molecule.

Indicators

Indicators are substances whose color depends on the acidity of an aqueous solution, called its pH. Litmus is a colored extract from certain lichens (LY-kuhnz; organisms made up of an alga and a fungus). In acid, litmus is red; in a base, it changes to a blue form when it loses a hydrogen ion. The change happens at pH7, which is neutral. Phenolphthalein (FEE-nol-THAL-EEN) is a synthetic (produced artificially) compound that is colorless in acidic and neutral solutions, yet turns a reddish violet color in basic solutions.

LOOK CLOSER

Acidity and pH

The acidity of a solution depends on the concentration of hydrogen ions. Scientists measure this concentration in moles per liter. A mole is the number of atoms of an element that has a mass, in grams, equal to the mass number of that element. Neutral water contains 0.0000001 moles of hydrogen ions in each liter because a minute proportion of the water molecules split up to form hydrogen ions and hydroxide ions: $H_2O \rightarrow H^+ + OH^-$. Acids increase the concentration of hydrogen atoms from this value.

In 1909, Danish biochemist Søren Sørensen (1868–1939) proposed the pH scale to represent the vast range of hydrogen-ion concentrations in acidic and alkaline solutions, based on negative powers of 10. Just as 10^2 represents 10 x 10 = 100, so 10^{-2} represents 1 divided by 10^2, which is $\frac{1}{100}$ or 0.01. The concentration of hydrogen ions, H⁺, in a solution is related to its pH in the following way: $H^+ = 10^{-pH}$.

Neutral water, whose hydrogen-ion concentration is 10^{-7} (0.0000001) moles per liter, has pH value 7. A strong acid solution that contains one mole of hydrogen ions per liter has pH value 0, since $1 = 10^0$. A strong alkali that contains one mole of hydroxide ions per liter has pH14, since the hydroxide ions reduce the hydrogen-ion concentration to 10^{-14} by reacting with some of them to form water. Some examples of hydrogen-ion concentrations and pH values are listed below.

Solution	Moles of H⁺ per liter	pH	
Acid rain	0.001–0.01	3–2	acidic
Vinegar	0.001	3	acidic
Rain	0.0000025	5.6	slightly acidic
Water (pure)	0.0000001	7	neutral
Blood	0.00000004	7.4	slightly basic
Seawater	0.000000005	8.3	basic

The approximate pH of a solution can be measured by testing with a variety of indicators that change colors at different values of pH.

CHECK THESE OUT!
✔CHEMICAL REACTION ✔SALTS

Acoustics

The science of how sound is produced and transmitted

S ound can bring real pleasure or real pain. There is a big difference between a Mozart symphony and a relentless pneumatic drill. Music is a type of sound that people want to listen to, and the insides of some buildings are designed to take this into account. Some noises, on the other hand, are types of sound that everyone can do without. Highways and construction sites sometimes use equipment to reduce the noise they send into the environment. There is a whole science concerned with how sound is produced, how music is enhanced, and how noise is minimized. This science is called acoustics (uh-KOOS-tiks). This comes from the Greek word *akoustikos*, which means, "related to hearing."

How sound travels

Sound is a type of wave, like light waves or waves on the ocean. Sound shares many of the properties of other types of waves. If a person stands about 100 feet (33 m) from a wall and claps their hands, a short time later an echo can be heard of the sound that is made. The sound is reflected from the wall just as light is reflected from a mirror. If someone stands at an angle to the wall and shouts, the sound wave will be reflected at an angle, too, just like a pool ball bouncing off a pool-table cushion.

In some ways, however, sound seems quite unlike light. For example, if someone leaves a door open, they can hear people talking in another room even though they cannot see them. This happens because the wavelength of sound is much greater than the wavelength of light. Sound spreads out around an open doorway and effectively bends around corners in a process called diffraction (dih-FRAK-shuhn).

Just like waves on the water, sound waves can interfere (combine) with one another. Sometimes two sound waves join together so that the crests (highest points) of one wave line up with the

HIGHLIGHTS

◆ Acoustics is based on an understanding of how sound waves travel.

◆ Acoustics engineers work to improve the sound quality in places such as concert halls and churches and to reduce the noise produced by construction sites, airports, and so on.

◆ Unwanted sound can be reduced indoors by carefully designing the size and shape of a room and the materials from which it is made.

◆ Outdoors, noise can be reduced by controlling the sound at its source, interrupting its transmission with barriers, or preventing it from reaching the listener, with earplugs or thickened glazing.

crests of the other. This is called reinforcement, or constructive interference, and produces a new wave much bigger than the original. Other times, two waves combine so the crests of one meet the troughs (lowest points) of the other. This is called cancellation, or destructive interference, and can wipe out both of the original waves. Acoustics involves using these properties of sound, with the sound-absorbing and reflecting properties of materials, to enrich music or speech in concert halls and auditoriums and to reduce unwanted noise in the environment.

Indoor acoustics

Acoustics is best known as a branch of architecture (the work of planning buildings) concerned with designing buildings that enhance (increase or improve) certain sounds in certain ways. This is also called architectural acoustics or room acoustics. Concert halls, conference centers, churches, and rock music venues are just a few of the buildings that benefit from these carefully researched building techniques.

The most important thing for architects to bear in mind when they are designing a concert hall is the way in which sound will travel from the stage to the people in the audience. Some sound waves will travel in straight lines, but others will reach the listeners' ears indirectly after bouncing off walls and other obstacles. Because the indirect sound always travels farther than the direct sound, people hear it as

The glass-fiber wedges in a sound chamber prevent sound from being reflected. This is tested by a wired-up dummy.

an echo or reverberation (rih-vuhr-buh-RAY-shuhn; resounding series of echoes). The quality of the sound depends on the length of time between the original sound and the reverberation. In a living room with lots of cushions and carpets, the reverberation time is very short; in a large indoor swimming pool with lots of hard surfaces, it is much longer. A moderate amount of reverberation gives a rich sound in a concert hall, but too much reverberation means the direct sounds and their echoes blur together.

Many different factors affect the reverberation time and the quality of the sound. These include the size and shape of the room and the materials from which it is built and furnished. One very important consideration is the way in which human bodies absorb sound. A full concert hall will sound very different from an empty one. For this reason, chairs are usually made from substances that make them absorb sound just like a person's body. This ensures that the hall sounds the same no matter how many or how few people are in it.

Outdoor acoustics

Unwanted sounds that are produced in the open air are referred to as noise pollution. Environmental acoustics is concerned with using the properties of sound to reduce noise and the nuisance that it causes.

Noise involves a sound being produced in one place, transmitted through the air, and received in another place. Controlling noise means interrupting the sound at one of these three points. The most obvious way to reduce noise is to stop it at the source. Automobiles and motorcycles are fitted with silencers (devices that make an engine quieter). Noise can also be interrupted during transmission. Large earth barriers called bunds are sometimes built next to highways to reflect traffic noise away from houses. Finally, noise can be removed at the point where it would normally be heard. Houses built near airports are usually fitted with thick double-glazed windows to cut the noise from jets taking off and landing. Construction workers usually wear ear protectors to prevent noise from entering their ears and damaging their hearing.

STORY OF SCIENCE

Whispering Chambers

Buildings with large domes have areas that are sometimes called whispering galleries or chambers because people find that they can stand on one side of the dome and overhear whispered conversations on the other. Sound bounces off the dome from the speaker to the listener just like light bounces off a concave (inward-curving) mirror. In the Capitol Building, the old House of Representatives chamber also acts as a whispering chamber—the curved surfaces bounce conversations from one side to the other.

This effect can be demonstrated by using two opened umbrellas. If two people stand 20 feet (6 m) apart with their umbrellas tilted with their undersides toward each other, and one whispers into his umbrella, the other should be able to hear the sound reflected off her own umbrella quite clearly.

The Capitol Building in Washington, D.C.

Noise cannot always be reduced so simply. People have to work somewhere, and work usually produces noise. One solution involves planning towns and cities so that residential areas are separated from the places where noisy industries go about their business. Similarly, airports can redirect air traffic so it flies over less-populated areas. Pressure from local communities can be used to persuade aircraft designers to produce quieter airplanes. Noise complaints led authorities to ban the supersonic (traveling faster than sound) aircraft called Concorde from landing in New York in the 1970s and has led to tight restrictions on how the aircraft operates ever since. Airplane noise is not just a problem on the ground. Jet fighter pilots sometimes wear headphones that sample the cockpit noise waves, flip them over (so crests become troughs and vice versa), and then add them to the original waves to cancel the noise out completely.

Measuring noise

Acoustic engineers can reduce noise only if they know how much noise there is to begin with. To do this they use very sensitive instruments to measure noise. The standard instrument is called a sound-level meter or a decibel (DES-uh-buhl) meter because it measures noise in units called decibels (dB). The noise in a quiet house would measure roughly 35 to 40 dB, whereas a jet airplane could reach 120 dB. The difference between these sounds is very much greater than it might appear, because an increase of 10 dB means that people report a doubling of the sound intensity.

If acoustics engineers are designing sound equipment, such as radio antennas or loudspeakers, they need to use rooms from which echoes (reverberations) have been eliminated. The walls and floors of these rooms are usually fitted with materials (such as foam pyramids) that absorb all sound and so prevent any sound waves from being reflected. Rooms designed in this way are called dead rooms or anechoic (an-eh-KOH-ik) chambers, which means they produce no echoes. Recording studios, by contrast, are designed to have enough reverberation to produce a richer sound. This explains why rock bands have sometimes recorded songs in bathrooms, where the hard surfaces reflect sound well and produce pleasing reverberations.

CHECK THESE OUT!
✔SOUND ✔ULTRASOUND

Aerodynamics

The science of gas motion around objects

Why is it that trucks that move at low speeds can be box-shaped and bulky, but high-speed jet airplanes must be dart-shaped and sleek? The faster a plane tries to fly, the more drag there is to slow it down. Drag is also called air resistance, and it is the push of air against a moving object. Unless a plane is aerodynamic (designed to slice through the air most easily), it will not move fast enough to stay in the sky. Aerodynamic design is based on the idea of reducing drag to a minimum. It is essential to the performance of everything from airplanes and trains to cycling helmets. It is as important for helping track athletes win races as for getting the space shuttle back to Earth.

The problem of drag

Scientists once believed that heavy objects fell to Earth more quickly than lighter objects. It was an easy mistake to make. If a rock and feather are dropped from the same height, the rock will reach Earth much sooner than the feather. Air resistance slows the feather down because of its shape. If a pebble with the same weight as the feather is dropped at the same time as the rock, they will reach Earth at the same time.

Air resistance is central to aerodynamics. If someone walks slowly, they do not even notice drag. If they run or travel in a convertible car, they become much more aware of the wind whistling past. At supersonic speeds (speeds greater than the speed of sound), drag is so great that it can rip an airplane apart if it is not built from immensely strong materials.

Drag also affects cars, trucks, and trains. At low speeds, a car uses most of its fuel to move its own weight and wheels along the road. The faster it

goes, however, the more fuel is needed to overcome drag. The same applies to trains. Freight trains are usually square and bulky because they travel only at low speeds. High-speed trains, such as the Japanese Bullet train, need to be much more aerodynamic.

To travel faster, cyclists wear aerodynamically shaped helmets and bend low over the handlebars. This reduces their air resistance.

HIGHLIGHTS

◆ Aerodynamics is concerned with reducing air resistance (drag) that can slow down a moving object or vehicle.

◆ Smooth, sleek objects cut through the air better than box-shaped ones.

◆ Aerodynamic design of vehicles becomes more and more important at higher speeds.

◆ The aerodynamic shape of airfoils keeps airplanes and helicopters in the sky and helps race cars hug the track at high speeds.

*The Blackbird, the U.S. spy plane.
Its aerodynamic shape and ability to
reach high altitudes (where the air is thinner)
allow it to travel at supersonic speeds.*

Principles of aerodynamics

Just as a pebble cuts through air faster than a feather, so certain body designs for airplanes, trains, and automobiles are better at defeating drag than others. Sharp edges are generally better than blunt ones, and slanting, angled bodies are better than box-shaped ones.

In the early part of the 20th century, automobile designers found they could make cars travel faster and more economically using a technique called streamlining. Square car bodies were replaced by rounded ones shaped rather like an airfoil (the curved wing of an airplane). Some land-speed record-breaking automobiles from the mid-20th century were simply giant airfoils with a small passenger compartment in the middle. Today, cars still use the airfoil shape, with a rounded front end and a long back end. The reason is simple: it is the best aerodynamic shape for vehicles traveling at this speed.

How aerodynamics helps airplanes fly

Birds fly by flapping their wings, but airplanes stay in the air with wings that never move. The secret of an airplane's flight lies in the shape of its airfoil wings. They have a curved upper surface that trails to a point at the back and a much straighter lower surface.

When air passes around an airfoil, the front edge splits the airstream in two, with part of the stream being directed over the top of the airfoil and part being directed under the bottom. Because the top surface is curved, the air that moves over it travels faster than the air that moves under the bottom surface. Fast-moving air has a lower pressure than slow-moving air, so the air pressure is greater underneath an airfoil. The difference in air pressure causes an upward force on the airfoil called lift. The faster the airplane moves, the greater the lift. When it reaches a certain speed, the lift is greater than the weight of the airplane, and the whole airplane takes off.

In fact, there are always four forces acting on an airplane when it is up in the sky. These are lift, weight, thrust, and drag. Lift created by the airfoils pushes the airplane upward, while the

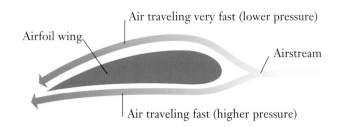

*The airfoil shape of an airplane wing creates
a difference in pressure that lifts the wing up.*

weight of the airplane pushes it down. Thrust from the airplane's engines pushes it forward through the sky, while drag pulls it backward.

As airplanes traveled faster and faster, engineers found they needed to use increasingly ingenious methods of aerodynamic design. Supersonic airplanes, flying faster than the speed of sound (760 miles per hour or 1,225 km/h), must be particularly aerodynamic. One of the best known supersonic airplanes is Concorde, the transatlantic passenger jet designed jointly by engineers in Britain and France. Concorde has an aluminum alloy skin that sheds the tremendous heat generated at supersonic speeds. It has very thin wings, which are gracefully curved at the front to minimize drag and reduce fuel consumption. Concorde also has a very long pointed nose. To make sure that the pilot can see properly during take-off and landing, this nose pivots up and down.

Aircraft are considered to be hypersonic if they will travel at least five times the speed of sound (3,800 miles per hour or 6,125 km/h). The space shuttle *Orbiter* (the main part of the space shuttle) is an example of a hypersonic plane. Unlike Concorde, *Orbiter* has a ball-shaped nose and wide jet nozzles. This is because this shape is the most aerodynamic at hypersonic speeds.

Just as temperature is a problem at supersonic speeds, it is also a problem for the hypersonic *Orbiter*. On reentry to Earth's atmosphere, drag generates so much heat that it could melt the craft completely. To prevent this, different parts of the *Orbiter* are covered in different kinds of protective materials. The bottom is covered in black, heat-resistant silica (SIH-lih-kuh; a hard, glassy material) tiles that are 1 to 5 inches (2.5 to 12.7 cm) thick.

Pioneers of aerodynamics

The modern science of aerodynamics is based on a branch of physics called fluid dynamics, which literally means fluids in motion. Fluid dynamics explains how fluids (liquids and gases) behave when they move about; aerodynamics looks more specifically at what happens when gases move over objects or objects move through gases.

LOOK CLOSER

Inside a Wind Tunnel

Wind-tunnel testing is one of the most important stages of trying out the aerodynamics of a new design. The idea was used to test aircraft wings by German physicist Ludwig Prandtl in 1909. It involves placing a prototype (a working model) into a stream of air created by a powerful fan. Smoke may be blown into the airstream so the path of the air around the model shows up clearly. The model's behavior can be tested at different speeds by making the fan blow air faster or slower. Wind tunnels have been used to test everything from bicycle helmets to the shape of the space shuttle.

Strips of tape show how air flows over a car in a wind tunnel.

EVERYDAY SCIENCE

How Helicopters Fly

Helicopters do not look especially streamlined, but aerodynamics plays a key role in keeping them in the air. Airplanes produce lift using their airfoil wings. However, unlike an airplane, a helicopter generates its lift with the spinning rotor mounted on its roof. This has two or more separate blades, each of which is shaped like an airfoil. As the blades spin, they generate lift. The pilot can tilt the blades so they cut into the air at a steeper angle. This generates extra lift at takeoff. The pilot can also tilt the entire rotor in any direction to make the helicopter fly that way. This explains how a helicopter can fly forward, backward, or sideways. When a helicopter just hovers in the air, the lift created by the rotor blades exactly balances the weight of the craft.

Fluid dynamics was first studied by Swiss mathematician and philosopher Daniel Bernoulli (1700–1782). Bernoulli worked out that fluids have reduced pressure when they move at higher speeds. This was the theory of the airfoil and, in a sense, all the airplanes that have ever been built stem from Bernoulli's early work.

Other scientists also played a key role. Italian inventor Leonardo da Vinci (1452–1519) sketched hundreds of pictures of birds' wings and artificial flying machines. He greatly advanced the understanding of how people could take to the air. One of his most famous designs is much like a modern helicopter but was drawn over 400 years before the helicopter was perfected. Leonardo's ideas were based largely on his extraordinary imagination, but practical flying machines need an understanding of the physics of flight as well as creative ideas. British inventor Sir George Cayley (1773–1857) made two important advances. He realized that a flying machine needed a rigid body and that the method of providing lift (upward force) could be separated from the method of providing thrust (forward force). This insight meant that the inventors of flying machines did not have to copy the flapping wings of birds.

U.S. aviators Wilbur and Orville Wright finally made the first powered flight in 1903. However, scientists and engineers continued to study how airplanes fly and stay in the air. Shortly after the Wright brothers' flight, British engineer Frederick Lanchester (1868–1946) and German physicist Ludwig Prandtl (1875–1953) explained in detail how lift occurs on an airfoil. Their ideas were enormously influential and contributed greatly to modern aircraft design.

The aerodynamics of sport

Aerodynamics is most useful at the high speeds needed for airplane flight, but it is also important on the ground. It has become a particularly important technique in all kinds of sports, where even the slightest aerodynamic advantage can help athletes beat their competitors.

Race cars are as aerodynamic as airplanes and have airfoils positioned at key points on their structures. Unlike airplane wings, these are designed to provide downward lift (called ground effect) for safety, so the cars hug the track better at high speeds.

Skiers and bobsled competitors wear aerodynamic clothing and tuck themselves down to reduce air resistance. Olympic cyclists use similar tactics, and most wear teardrop-shaped helmets and ride carefully streamlined bicycles. Olympic swimmers also have to consider fluid dynamics, because the drag of water resistance is very much greater than air resistance. Some swimmers shave their heads and bodies because even a small amount of hair can slow them down.

CHECK THESE OUT!
✔FORCE ✔FRICTION ✔GAS ✔LIQUID
✔MECHANICS ✔MOMENTUM ✔MOTION
✔NEWTONIAN PHYSICS ✔PHYSICS

Africa

At nearly three-quarters the size of Asia, Africa is the world's second-largest continent. It covers 20 percent of Earth's land area and is almost surrounded by water. On the north side of Africa is the Mediterranean Sea. To the east is the Indian Ocean and to the west, the Atlantic Ocean. In the south, the continent comes to a point at Cape Agulhas. The equator runs across the middle of Africa, and most of the continent lies within the tropics (either side of the equator). There are huge desert areas in the north and southwest of Africa, where very few people live. Africa contains only 10 percent of the world's population.

A miner drills for gold in South Africa. There are also important diamond mines in South Africa.

Geology

Roughly 200 million years ago, Africa was part of a supercontinent called Pangaea (pan-JEE-uh). Pangaea split in two, forming Laurasia and Gondwana. Laurasia moved northward to form North America, Europe, and Asia. In Gondwana, South America began to separate from Africa about 135 million years ago. Africa became a separate continent about five million years ago, when the Red Sea and the Gulf of Aden opened up. Part of this movement spread south into Africa, forming the Great Rift Valley.

Most of the rocks of Africa are very old—much more than 1.3 billion years. In South Africa, tiny fossils (preserved evidence of past life) of single-cell organisms and chemical traces of life have been dated at 3.5 billion years old.

The highest mountains in Africa are relatively recent in terms of Earth's history. They are volcanic peaks bordering the Great Rift Valley. Kilimanjaro, in northeast Tanzania, is 19,340 feet (5,899 m) high, and Mount Kenya is 17,058 feet (5,203 m) high. The summits of the Ethiopian Highlands rise higher than 15,000 feet (4,575 m). Although they lie very close to the equator, the tops of Kilimanjaro and Mount Kenya are permanently snow-capped. On the west coast, near the equator, the Cameroon Highlands are also volcanic. They rise to 13,353 feet (4,073 m). The Drakensberg Mountains, on the east coast of South Africa, reach 11,425 feet (3,485 m).

HIGHLIGHTS

◆ Some of the rocks in Africa are billions of years old and are a rich source of minerals.

◆ Some of the oldest life-forms yet discovered on Earth have been found in 3.5-billion-year-old rocks in southern Africa.

◆ Fossil remains of the earliest ancestors of humankind have been found in the Great Rift Valley. They are around 3.5 million years old.

◆ The Nile River is the longest in the world, and its source, Lake Victoria, is the second largest lake.

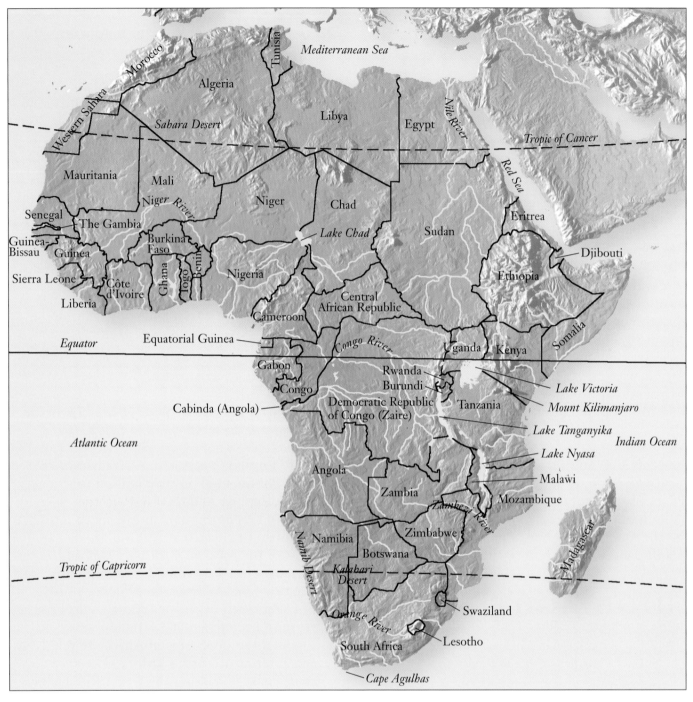

The continent of Africa.

The other major mountain range is the Atlas Mountains in northwest Africa. These mountains were formed when the landmass of Africa moved northward and caused Earth's crust to fold. Their parallel ridges run from southwest to northeast, through Morocco, Algeria, and Tunisia. They reach a maximum height of 13,665 feet (4,168 m) at Jebel Toubkal in Morocco. Two isolated mountain areas occur in the middle of the Sahara Desert. These are the Ahaggar Mountains of southern Algeria (9,842 feet or 3,002 m), and the Tibesti Mountains of northwestern Chad (11,204 feet or 3,417 m). The lowest points in Africa are below sea level. Examples are the Qattara Depression in northwestern Egypt and the Chott Merouane in northeastern Algeria. The lowest point of all is Lake Assal in Djibouti, which is 502 feet (153 m) below sea level.

Apart from this, most of the land surface of Africa is a landscape of hills, plains, and plateaus (pla-TOHZ; high, flat areas). In the north and west, there are wide low plains along the coasts of west Africa, Libya, and Egypt. The south and east of the continent are generally higher.

Rivers and lakes

Africa's great rivers have often been the easiest way to travel from one region to another. In drier areas, river water is important for irrigation (channeling water to areas of dry land). In addition, many rivers have been dammed to provide hydroelectric power (production of electricity by water power).

The Nile is the world's longest river. It flows 3,473 miles (5,588 km) from Lake Victoria in Uganda, through Sudan and Egypt, to reach the Mediterranean Sea at Alexandria. For more than 5,000 years the annual Nile floods have been an essential part of Egyptian agriculture, bringing water and fertile silt (fine mud) to the dry land.

Other major African rivers include the Congo, the Niger, the Zambezi, and the Orange. The Congo—alternatively known as the Zaire River—is 2,716 miles (4,370 km) long. It rises in the highlands of northern Zambia, and its drainage basin (the land drained by the river system) covers more than 10 percent of the continent. It flows through the Democratic Republic of Congo in a huge curve and reaches the Atlantic Ocean on the border between Angola and the Democratic Republic of Congo. The Niger is 2,600 miles (4,183 km) long, rising on the border between Sierra Leone and Guinea. It flows

LOOK CLOSER

Great Rift Valley

The Great Rift Valley in eastern Africa is one of the world's most impressive geological features. It is a huge split in the continental crust, running 3,000 miles (4,827 km) from the Red Sea at Djibouti to the coast of the Indian Ocean in Mozambique. It is a parallel-sided depression averaging 2,000 to 3,000 feet (610 to 915 m) deep and 30 to 40 miles (48 to 64 km) across.

The rift extends northward along the Red Sea and continues through Israel and Jordan, marked by the Dead Sea and the valley of the Jordan River. Southward, the rift splits into two in southern Ethiopia, with the eastern arm ending in Tanzania.

The Rift Valley was formed between 6 and 1 million years ago. Its formation was accompanied by a great deal of volcanic activity. There are many volcanoes, some extinct and others still active, along its edges. The dormant peak of Mount Kilimanjaro is the highest on the African continent.

The Great Rift Valley is renowned for its varied wildlife. The floor of the valley contains a number of long, narrow lakes, the largest two being Tanganyika and Malawi. Some of the smaller lakes are shallow and salty. Lake Nakuru, on the border between Kenya and Tanzania, is a soda lake, famous for its population of flamingos.

EVERYDAY SCIENCE

The very early volcanic rocks of Africa, more than a billion years old, are a rich source of minerals. Around 57 percent of the continent's land surface is made up of these rocks. Africa possesses 75 percent of the world's diamonds and more than half of its gold, manganese, and phosphate rock. Africa is also a major producer of chromium, aluminum, copper, iron ore, uranium, petroleum, and other economically important minerals.

northeast into Mali, then makes a curve southeastward before turning south to flow into the Atlantic Ocean in the Gulf of Guinea.

The Zambezi is the longest river of southern Africa. It flows 1,700 miles (2,735 km) from northwest Zambia, plunging over the Victoria Falls, reaching the Indian Ocean in Mozambique. The Orange River rises in the Drakensberg range of South Africa and flows westward for 1,300 miles (2,092 km) to the Atlantic Ocean.

Lake Victoria, the source of the Nile River, is the second largest lake in the world (the largest is Lake Superior). It has a surface area of 26,800 square miles (69,412 sq km), lies on the plateau of Tanzania, and is only 265 feet (81 m) deep. There are several other huge lakes on the floor of the Great Rift Valley. Lake Tanganyika is the

DISCOVERERS

The Leakey Family

Many fossils of the earliest human beings have been found in the Great Rift Valley. At the beginning of the 20th century, the search for early human fossils began in South Africa. However, the search moved to the Great Rift Valley after a series of major discoveries between 1959 and 1963. A team was led by the Anglo-Kenyan archaeologists Louis Leakey (1903–1972) and Mary Leakey (1913–1996, below). In the Olduvai Gorge in north Tanzania, members of the team uncovered the fossil remains of two human-like species who lived around 1.75 million years ago.

The Leakeys' son Richard (born 1944) continued his parents' work, and in 1975, at Koobi Fara on the border between Ethiopia and Tanzania, a team of his colleagues found the fossil bones of at least 13 individuals, dated at 3.5 million years old.

world's second deepest lake (after Lake Baikal) with a depth of 4,710 feet (1,437 m). Other lakes include lake Nyasa in Malawi and lakes Albert, Edward, and Kivu (all on the eastern border of the Democratic Republic of Congo). The largest lake outside the Great Rift Valley is Lake Chad on the southern fringe of the Sahara.

Climate and vegetation

The continent of Africa stretches roughly equal distances north and south of the equator. The northernmost point is Ras ben Sekka in Tunisia, 37 degrees north; and the southernmost point is Cape Agulhas, 34 degrees south. The climatic zones are therefore roughly similar on each side of the equator. However, they are also affected by mountains and deserts, the direction of the winds, and the cooling effects of the ocean. For example, north of the equator, around the Tropic of Cancer, Africa is at its widest; therefore, in the interior, the ocean is far away. In the south, however, below the Tropic of Capricorn, the continent narrows to a point, and the influence of the ocean is greater.

Central Africa, between 5 degrees north and south, has a typical equatorial climate. It is blanketed in thick rain forest and is hot, humid, and rainy all year round. North and south of this zone is a tropical monsoon climate. It is hot and wet, with a regular, limited rainy season. On the east of central Africa, the climate is affected by altitude and the seasonal monsoon winds. For example, Kenya's central plateau has an average height of 3,000 to 5,000 feet (914 to 1,524 m) with mountains reaching to over 17,000 feet (5,185 m). Although the coast has an equatorial climate, the interior is cooler and less humid.

Farther from the equator, the climate becomes drier. The forest thins out to scrub (short trees and bushes) and the open grasslands called savannas. In the southeastern half, the southeasterly trade winds from the Indian Ocean bring rain to the east side of the continent. A truly dry climate is therefore found only in the Kalahari and Namib deserts of the southwest. In the north, however, the trade winds blow from Asia and are already dry, so northern Africa has the Sahara Desert and semidesert Sahel.

The Sahara is the world's largest desert, covering an area of about 3.5 million square miles (9,065,000 sq km)—as large as the whole United States. Day temperatures as high as 122°F (50°C) are regularly recorded in central Algeria. To the south, in the Tibesti Mountains of Chad, the night temperature can be as low as 5°F (–15°C). Huge areas of the Sahara have no rain for years on end.

CHECK THESE OUT!
✔CLIMATE ✔CONTINENT ✔DESERT ✔DROUGHT
✔GEOGRAPHY ✔GEOLOGY ✔HYDROLOGY
✔LANDFORM ✔MONSOON ✔ORE ✔PLATE TECTONICS
✔PRECAMBRIAN TIME ✔RIVER ✔TROPICAL REGION

Air Pressure

The force that air molecules exert through their constant, random movements

Earth's gravity pulls things to the planet's surface like a giant magnet. Gravity does not just affect large everyday objects such as cars and people; it also exerts a pull on tiny objects such as air molecules (atoms bonded together). The Earth's gravity holds a layer of vital gases (the atmosphere) to the planet, without which life could not exist. The gas molecules are not static, but are in constant motion, moving about randomly like bumper cars, crashing into one another and any objects that are in their way. Each collision exerts a tiny force, and it is this that causes air (atmospheric) pressure.

A barograph measures air pressure. The central part moves with changes in air pressure and causes the pointer to record changes on the roll of paper.

HIGHLIGHTS

◆ Air pressure is caused by air molecules colliding with one another.

◆ Air pressure falls off rapidly with altitude as Earth's atmosphere gets thinner. Virtually all of the atmosphere exists in a band 30 miles (48 km) above sea level.

◆ Barometers are used to measure air pressure. Torricellian barometers use a long tube filled with mercury; aneroid barometers have a sealed box and a moving pointer.

◆ Barometers can be used to make weather forecasts, because high pressure usually means dry and fair weather, and low pressure means wet and stormy weather.

The red line shows how air pressure decreases quite sharply above the point where 90 percent of the atmosphere's air molecules lie, at a height of about 9 miles (14 km).

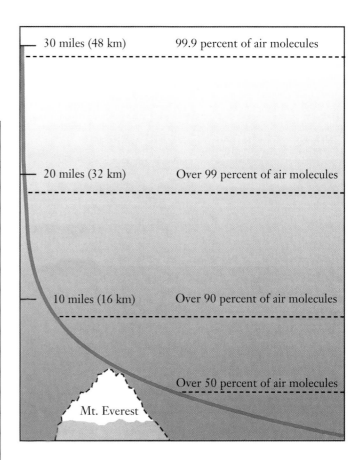

EVERYDAY SCIENCE

Barometers

A barometer (buh-RAHM-uht-uhr) is a scientific instrument used for measuring air pressure. The first barometer was developed in 1643 by Italian physicist Evangelista Torricelli (1608–1642). Quite unlike the barometers that hang on people's walls, Torricelli's barometer was based on a long sealed tube filled with mercury, a liquid metal. The tube stood upright, like a rocket, with the sealed end at the top, in a shallow bowl containing more mercury. Torricelli found that atmospheric pressure acting on the mercury in the bowl could hold up a column of mercury in the tube (not unlike the mercury in a thermometer). The higher the air pressure, the higher the mercury rose up the tube.

Although mercury barometers like this are very accurate, they are not practical for everyday use. The barometers people have in their homes work in a different way. They have a tightly sealed metal box filled with air that is connected to an arrangement of springs and levers. Changes in air pressure squeeze the box or allow it to expand by a very tiny amount. As the box changes slightly in shape, it pushes a lever connected to the barometer's pointer, which rises and falls as the changes in air pressure either squeeze the box or allow it to expand. Because the box is called an aneroid (AN-uhr-OYD) cell, this type of barometer is called an aneroid barometer.

Torricellian and aneroid barometers both date from the 17th century (although aneroid barometers are so intricate that they were constructed only from the 19th century onward). Today, scientists still use instruments based on these early designs. However, they also use instruments with digital readouts, which are much more accurate than analog instruments (those with a moving pointer).

One very common modern barometer is called a barograph. Similar to an aneroid barometer, it has a pen fixed to its pointer and makes a continuous record of the air pressure on a moving roll of paper.

Atmospheric pressure

Atmospheric pressure is caused by the weight of air molecules pressing downward. This is why atmospheric pressure is so much greater in low-lying areas than at the top of a mountain. Atmospheric pressure falls off very quickly with altitude (height above Earth's surface). At a height of around 5 miles (8 km), the atmosphere has fallen to around half the thickness that it has at sea level. Over 99.9 percent of the atmosphere's air molecules exist in a band stretching upward from Earth's surface to a height of 30 miles (48 km). Nevertheless, there is no point at which the atmosphere stops abruptly.

The way in which pressure varies with altitude has some interesting effects. The temperature at which liquids boil falls with pressure, so water boils at a slightly lower temperature atop a mountain than at sea level. The reduced air pressure at very high altitudes also explains why high-flying airplanes need pressurized cabins. These keep the pressure inside them at artificially increased levels to ensure that passengers can feel comfortable and breathe enough oxygen in the thin air of high altitudes.

Pressure and density

Atmospheric pressure is caused by collisions between air molecules moving about. The more molecules there are, the more collisions they make and the greater the pressure they exert. This means that areas of greater air density (with more air molecules) are at a higher pressure than areas of lower density (with fewer air molecules).

Air density also varies—the hotter it is, the less dense the air becomes. High air pressure typically goes with cold air, and low pressure with warm air. Air seems heavier and thicker on humid days (when there is a lot of water vapor in the atmosphere). However, the more water vapor there is in the air, the less dense the air itself is.

Measuring pressure

Pressure is defined as the amount of force acting over an area. If someone presses his or her thumb against a wooden table, no impression is made on the wood at all. However, if someone presses just as hard against a pin on a table, the tip sinks into the wood. Although the same force is used, it is concentrated over a smaller area. It is the greater pressure that pushes the pin into the wood.

Pressure is measured by instruments called barometers. The units in which it is measured are simply units of force divided by units of area. Pressure is commonly measured in pounds (a unit of force) per square inch (a unit of area). Scientists measure pressure in metric units called pascals, named for French mathematician and philosopher Blaise Pascal (1623–1662).

Forecasting the weather

Predicting the weather from one day to the next is difficult. Even though forecasters use some of the most powerful supercomputers in the world, they still find it difficult to predict the weather accurately. Many people have a

Blaise Pascal, with a calculator that he invented when he was only 19.

simple barometer at home, and it can be used to make rough but often surprisingly accurate forecasts about the weather.

Barometers are sometimes labeled not just with pressure measurements but also with descriptions of the weather that goes with them. The high-pressure end of a barometer is usually marked fair and dry, while the low-pressure end is marked stormy and rainy.

Why are high and low pressures linked with these different types of weather? Wind flows from high- to low-pressure zones. When it reaches the low-pressure zone, the air rises. Rising air cools, the moisture in it condenses (turns from gas into liquid), and clouds and rain are produced. The opposite happens in high-pressure zones. When air moves from a high-pressure zone to a low-pressure zone, it creates a partial vacuum. This sucks air into the area from up in the sky. Falling air warms up, causing clouds to evaporate (turn from a liquid into a gas), making the weather fair and dry.

CHECK THESE OUT!
✔ATMOSPHERE ✔CLIMATE
✔METEOROLOGY ✔WEATHER
✔WIND

Alkaloid

Coffee, cigarettes, cocaine, and strychnine have something in common—their effects are all due to alkaloids. The alkaloids are a large group of carbon-containing compounds that occur in plants and, more rarely, in animals. Apart from carbon, alkaloids also contain hydrogen, nitrogen, and oxygen.

The name *alkaloid* means alkali-like. This is because the nitrogen in alkaloids reacts with acids to form salts, just as, for example, the nitrogen in the alkali ammonia does. The salts of alkaloids dissolve in water. Methods for extracting alkaloids from chopped plants normally use a dilute solution of an acid in water to soak out the alkaloid salt. After soaking, the liquid is drained off and filtered to remove any remaining solids. Adding alkali to this solution usually changes the alkaloid salt back into an insoluble solid. The solid can then be filtered out of the liquid and dried. Alkaloids that are liquid at room temperature have to be distilled out of the mixture.

Poisons and medicines

Many alkaloids are poisonous in large doses. In some cases, the effect that makes the alkaloid poisonous also makes it useful in medicine.

A molecule of morphine, $C_{17}H_{19}NO_3$. Carbon (C) is shown in blue, hydrogen (H) is white, nitrogen (N) is light blue, and oxygen (O) is red.

Curare (kyoo-RAHR-ee) is an extremely poisonous extract from the bark of a South American woody vine *Strychnos toxifera*. It is used on the tips of arrows by peoples of the Amazon region of South America. Curare contains two alkaloids (curine and curarine) that paralyze the arrow's victim in seconds. Doctors use the paralyzing effect of synthetic curarine to relax patients' muscles for surgery. Cocaine is another alkaloid that has good and bad effects. Cocaine is extracted from the leaves of the coca plant, *Erythroxylon coca*. Coca leaves are traditionally used to relieve tiredness caused by high altitudes. Pure cocaine was used for many years as a dental anesthetic, since it causes local numbing when rubbed or injected into the gum. Cocaine is addictive, however, so dentists now use procaine (Novocaine) or lidocaine. Both these compounds are similar anesthetics to cocaine, but neither causes addiction.

Morphine and codeine both come from the opium poppy and are used in pain relief. Ergonovine, from the ergot fungus, *Claviceps purpurea*, causes blood vessels to contract and is used to reduce bleeding of the womb after childbirth. Vincristine and vinblastine, from *Vinca rosea*, are used in the treatment of cancer.

The biochemistry of alkaloids

Scientists know a great deal about how plants make alkaloids. The processes that are used to make synthetic medicines could easily make

HIGHLIGHTS

- ◆ Alkaloids occur in plants and some animals.
- ◆ Many alkaloids are highly poisonous.
- ◆ Some alkaloids can be used as medicines.

STORY OF SCIENCE

Opium and the Opiates

The opium poppy *Papaver somniferum* grows mainly in India and Turkey. The milky fluid that oozes from cuts in its unripe seed capsule forms a brown gum, opium resin, when it dries. Healers have prescribed this resin to treat pain for perhaps 6,000 years. In the first century C.E., Greek physician Dioscorides (around 40–90 C.E.) described the medicinal use of opium in his work *De Materia Medica*. At that time, opium would be taken with liquid or chewed as a gum. Opium contains a number of alkaloids, called opiates, that work on the body in a variety of ways. Opiates can relieve pain, reduce anxiety, and relax muscles. They have these properties because their molecules have similar shapes to endorphins, which the body produces to reduce pain. Opiates and endorphins both act as painkillers by blocking nerve impulses that carry pain signals to the brain. After a while, the use of opiates can cause addiction. Opium addiction only became a problem in the 17th century, when people discovered that smoking opium in pipes caused a sensation of pleasure.

In the 1810s, German chemist Friedrich Sertürner (1783–1841) became the first person to obtain a pure sample of morphine, which is the main component of opium gum. By the time of the U.S. Civil War (1861–1865), the hypodermic needle had been invented. Physicians believed that they would be able to treat pain by injecting pure morphine into casualties, thereby avoiding the addiction caused by smoking opium. They were wrong, however, as many of the casualties became addicted to the morphine.

In 1898, German pharmacologist Heinrich Dresser made an artificial alkaloid, heroin, by chemically altering morphine. Heroin is two to three times more powerful than morphine because it passes more easily through the barrier between the blood and the fluid around the brain and spinal cord. Once there, it breaks down into morphine and blocks nerve impulses. Heroin is a much more effective painkiller than morphine, and it is much more addictive. Morphine and other opiates are still widely used to control severe pain. However, the dosage of heroin must be controlled to prevent the patient from becoming addicted.

Resin is produced when the unripe seed capsule of an opium poppy is cut and the milk that oozed out is left to dry.

alkaloids. However, it is cheaper to extract (remove) alkaloids from their natural sources. In many cases, an alkaloid that comes from a plant can be changed into a synthetic material that is medically useful by a few simple chemical reactions, as is the case with cocaine. The effects that alkaloids have on the body are caused by one specific part of the alkaloid molecule fitting together with a molecule in the body. When an alkaloid has useful medical effects but harmful side effects, scientists make a range of compounds that have some molecular features in

common with the natural alkaloid. They then test the new molecules to discover whether they would be safer to use than the natural product. Procaine, for example, is a synthetic compound. Procaine works as an anesthetic because its molecules are similar enough to cocaine molecules to the nerve receptors that carry pain. Procaine is safer because it does not cause addiction.

CHECK THESE OUT!

✔ACID AND BASE ✔BIOCHEMISTRY ✔HYDROCARBON

Alloy

Mixture of a metal with one or more other elements that are usually metals

A pure metal rarely has the ideal properties for a given use. A combination of metals usually has better properties. In some cases, adding a small amount of a nonmetal to a metal improves its properties. Iron is a relatively soft metal that rusts easily and is attacked by acids. Tools made of pure iron would become blunt and damaged after very little use. By adding a small amount of carbon and other trace elements to iron, a steel is made that is hard enough to make tools. Adding nickel and chromium to iron makes a stainless steel that is ideal for cutlery, since it resists corrosion and tarnishing by substances in food that would attack pure iron. Bronze is a mixture of copper and tin that is stronger than either of those metals. Bronze was the first alloy (A-loy) to be made and used by humans. As long ago as 3000 B.C.E., bronze was produced by the peoples of the Middle East for making tools and weapons.

The structures of alloys

Alloys (A-loyz) differ from chemical compounds in that they do not contain elements in fixed, simple ratios. An alloy normally consists of one main metal into which other elements— the alloying agents—are mixed. In alloys where the atoms of alloying agents are of a similar size to atoms of the main metal, atoms of alloying agents fit into the main metal's crystal structure without causing too much disturbance. This is called a substitutional solid solution, since alloying atoms are substituted for atoms of the main metal in its own structure.

In another type of alloy, the alloying atoms are so much smaller than atoms of the main metal that they fit into spaces between the atoms in the main metal's lattice. These spaces are called interstices (in-TUHR-stuh-siz), and this type of alloy is called an interstitial (IN-tuhr-STISH-uhl)

Surgical instruments are made of stainless steel because it does not rust and can be cut to produce a very sharp edge.

HIGHLIGHTS

◆ Alloys are generally metal mixtures, but nonmetallic elements are also used.

◆ Materials in which the main metal is iron are called ferrous alloys.

◆ The chromium in stainless steels makes them resistant to corrosion, so they are widely used in cutlery, kitchen utensils, and surgical instruments.

solid solution. This type of structure is common when small nonmetal atoms, such as boron, carbon, hydrogen, and nitrogen, form alloys with metals such as iron, nickel, and chromium.

Ferrous alloys—steels

Ferrous alloys are materials in which the main metal is iron. Their name comes from *ferrum*, the Latin word for iron. Ferrous metals are the most widely used group of alloys because iron ore is so abundant in Earth's crust and because their properties vary widely, depending on the alloying agents.

Carbon steel is the simplest ferrous alloy. It is iron that contains only a small proportion of carbon but is much tougher than pure iron. Increasing the carbon content makes the steel harder but more brittle. Adding manganese to iron makes it easier to draw (pull) into useful shapes. Adding tungsten and molybdenum to iron makes it harder and better suited for making heavy-duty tools.

Stainless steels are mixtures of iron, nickel, and chromium that contain 11 to 36 percent chromium. The chromium makes these steels resistant to corrosion, so they are useful for making cutlery and surgical instruments.

Nonferrous alloys

Nonferrous alloys are mixtures based on metals other than iron. Bronze is a typical example. Modern bronze is mainly copper with a tin content of up to 25 percent. It is useful for making tools, musical instruments, and statues. A similar alloy, aluminum bronze, consists of copper with aluminum and small amounts of iron, nickel, manganese, and silicon. It is used to make aircraft parts. Brasses are also alloys of copper. Cartridge brass contains 30 percent zinc and is suitable for drawing into tubular shapes. High-tensile brass is copper alloyed with iron, manganese, and aluminum.

An important class of nonferrous alloys is formed by those that melt at lower temperatures. Solders (SAHL-duhrz) are alloys of tin with lead, silver, zinc, or even gold. Solders melt with the heat of a soldering iron, so they run into the gap between two metal surfaces. When the solder hardens, it joins the metals together. Alloys of tin

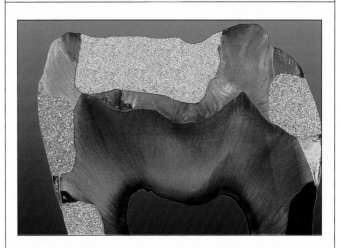

EVERYDAY SCIENCE

Amalgams

When dentists pack a metal filling into a newly drilled cavity, they use a form of alloy called an amalgam. Amalgams are alloys that the element mercury forms with other metals. Mercury has an unusual property for a metal—it is liquid at room temperature. Mercury can dissolve other metals to make liquid or pasty mixtures. The amalgam used for restorative dental work is made with powdered silver, tin, zinc, and copper. Just before the dentist fills the cavity, a dental technician mixes a small amount of the mixed-metal powder with a couple of drops of mercury. The mixture forms a paste that is soft enough to push into place but firm enough to stay put. The amalgam then hardens without shrinking or expanding. If it shrank, the filling would work loose; if it expanded, the tooth might shatter. Although mercury amalgam has been used for many decades, more and more fillings use pigmented epoxy resins (synthetic resins) that blend with tooth coloring and do not contain moderately toxic mercury metal.

with combinations of bismuth, lead, cadmium, and indium melt at temperatures as low as 117°F (47°C). These alloys are used in sprinkler systems for fire protection. If there is a fire, the heat melts an alloy plug that releases a flow of water to the sprinkler system.

CHECK THESE OUT!

✔CARBON ✔COPPER ✔IRON AND STEEL ✔MANGANESE ✔MERCURY, METAL ✔METAL ✔METALLURGY

Aluminum

A light and strong metal used in buildings, transportation, and the electrical industry

The most abundant (plentiful) metal in Earth's crust is aluminum, which makes up over 8 percent of the whole crust. Unlike some other metals, aluminum is not found free; it occurs generally as its oxide, alumina (uh-LOO-muh-nuh), or as aluminum silicate, the main part of clay. Sulfates of aluminum also occur. They are called alums, and it is from these that the metal gets its name. A common form of alum is potassium aluminum sulfate. Alums are used in dyes and to get small particles suspended in water to stick to each other so that they can be removed by filtration.

French chemists Antoine (1743–1794) and Marie (1758–1836) Lavoisier made a list of all the known elements, and they suggested the probable existence of aluminum. The metal was finally isolated in 1825 by Danish physicist Hans Christian Ørsted (1777–1851). It was not very pure, however, and two years later German chemist Friedrich Wöhler (1800–1882) produced much purer samples. Both methods, which used potassium metal, were very expensive.

In the early 1850s, French chemist Henri Sainte-Claire Deville (1818–1881) found a way to use sodium, which was cheaper, in place of potassium. Aluminum became commercially available soon afterward.

A cheaper method of extracting (removing) aluminum from its ore was developed in 1886 by U.S. chemist Charles Martin Hall (1863–1914) and French chemist Paul-Louis Héroult (1863–1914). Their method is still used today. Aluminum oxide is usually obtained by purifying bauxite, its most common ore. A steel tank lined with carbon is filled with another ore called cryolite, which is heated until it melts. Aluminum oxide is dissolved in the molten cryolite and a direct electric current (DC) is passed from the carbon lining to a carbon rod and round again. Aluminum collects on the bottom of the tank, where it is easily drawn off.

A mosque in Khartoum, Sudan, with a dome made of aluminum. Aluminum oxide forms naturally on the outside and prevents further corrosion.

The world's major bauxite-mining countries are Australia (25 percent), Jamaica (18 percent), Surinam (9 percent), Guinea (7 percent), Russia (6 percent), Guyana (5 percent), and the United States (3 percent). The annual production of aluminum is 21 million tons (19 million tonnes).

Properties of aluminum

In its pure form, aluminum is a soft and silvery metal. It reacts quickly with oxygen in the air, forming a thin and hard film of oxide (an oxygen compound). This protects it from further corrosion and makes aluminum a valuable building material.

Aluminum is a good conductor of heat and electricity. It can be drawn out into thin wires. Although its electrical conductivity is only about two-thirds that of copper, it is often used for power lines because it is both cheaper and lighter than copper.

In its pure form—without a coating of oxide—aluminum is a very reactive metal. When heated above 381.6°F (194.2°C), it will react violently with water. It is not easily attacked by sulfuric or nitric acids, which help to form the oxide coating, but it will dissolve in concentrated hydrochloric acid. It also reacts with strong alkalis, which easily dissolve the oxide.

Two compounds of aluminum, the sulfate and the hydroxide, are used to soften hard water. They get rid of magnesium and calcium, which coat the insides of kettles and water heaters.

Uses of aluminum

The major use of aluminum is in the construction (building) industry, where its strength, lightness, and resistance to corrosion are very important. Aluminum siding is used to protect the outside of millions of homes, as well as the outside walls of many skyscrapers. Other structures made of aluminum include doors, screens, window frames, and gutters.

The second largest use of aluminum is in the transportation industry. Many commercial and military airplanes are built almost entirely of the metal. Artificial satellites and space vehicles also use large amounts. Aluminum is widely used for bus and train parts, as well as automobile parts such as engine blocks, radiators, and wheels.

EVERYDAY SCIENCE

Recycling Aluminum

Although it is the most common metal in Earth's crust, economical sources of aluminum are slowly being used up. It has been calculated that, at current rates of consumption, there is enough for about 200 years. As the world's reserves of aluminum will clearly not last, it is extremely important to conserve the aluminum that has already been extracted. This is best done by recycling scrap aluminum products such as beverage cans. Communities can set up collection programs, and manufacturers can refund deposits on aluminum containers.

Recycling aluminum costs much less than extracting it from its ores and uses much less energy. Waste aluminum does not corrode away. This creates a garbage disposal problem with serious effects on the environment, so it makes good sense to recycle this particular metal.

Containers and packing materials for food and beverages, as well as many kitchen pans and appliances, are also made of aluminum. Aluminum electrical wires and cables have been used in homes, offices, and factories. Problems can arise, however, because aluminum expands and contracts more than copper in response to temperature changes, and connections can work loose. The use of aluminum wiring in construction is now discouraged.

CHECK THESE OUT!
✔ELEMENT ✔METAL

Antarctica

Earth's fifth-largest continent, found in the far south and surrounded by ocean

The vast continent found in the far south of Earth is called Antarctica. Covering an area of 5.5 million square miles (14 million sq km), it is Earth's fifth largest continent. An ice cap with an average thickness of 1.4 miles (2.3 km) covers almost all of Antarctica. This ice cap accounts for 70 to 90 percent of all the world's fresh water.

The thickness of its ice cap makes Antarctica by far the highest continent. With an average height of around 8,000 feet (2,400 m) above sea level, it is roughly three times higher than the other continents. The highest point is Vinson Massif, at 16,860 feet (5,139 m). The South Pole—the most southerly point on Earth—stands at a height of 9,200 feet (2,800 m).

HIGHLIGHTS

◆ Almost all of the continent of Antarctica is covered by a thick ice cap.

◆ Antarctic waters teem with life, but the climate on the mainland is too severe for large, land-based animals to survive.

◆ The continent of Antarctica was probably first sighted in 1820. In 1911, a Norwegian expedition led by Roald Amundsen was the first to reach the South Pole.

Climate

Antarctica is Earth's coldest continent. The lowest temperature recorded there is −128°F (−89°C), which is the lowest temperature ever recorded on Earth. It is far colder than the Arctic, which is occupied mostly by a relatively warm ocean, rather than a cold landmass. The seas around Antarctica have a warming influence on coastal areas, making the climate there milder than that inland. However, the coasts also experience some of the strongest winds ever felt on the planet, with gusts of up to 200 miles per hour (320 km/h).

Almost no rain falls in Antarctica, and the snow that falls there equals less than 1.9 inches (4.8 cm) of rainfall. Because Earth is tilted on its axis, almost all parts of Antarctica experience a period in summer when it is light for 24 hours a day, and a time in winter when the sun never rises. In spring, a hole appears in the ozone layer in the atmosphere above Antarctica. This is caused by the extreme cold and the chemicals that pollute Earth's atmosphere called chlorofluorocarbons (CFCs), which derive from discarded aerosol cans and refrigerators.

Origins of Antarctica

The Transantarctic Mountains divide the continent into West and East Antarctica. Each of the regions has a separate history. Some of the rocks of East Antarctica are two to three billion years old. Scientists have discovered that East Antarctica was once part of the

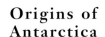

Emperor penguins live in Antarctica. They form large colonies, huddling together to keep warm in the cold weather.

DISCOVERERS

Who Discovered Antarctica?

The identity of the people who discovered Antarctica may never be certain. The continent was probably first sighted in 1820. In that year, expeditions from Russia, the United States, and Britain all sailed in Antarctic waters close to the mainland. However, it is unclear from the sailors' reports which of the vessels actually sighted land, rather than just sea ice.

supercontinent of Gondwana. About 200 million years ago, Gondwana broke apart, and East Antarctica drifted to its present position. It did not always lie so far south. Fossils (FAH-suhlz; preserved evidence of past life) found in East Antarctica include specimens of ancient ferns and dinosaurs, which prove that the landmass once lay in a much warmer part of the globe.

The rocks of West Antarctica are generally younger. They formed as part of the same geological process that produced the Andes Mountains in South America. Eventually, as the giant plates that form Earth's crust drifted very slowly about the globe, the two different landmasses were pushed together. Where the two masses of rock collided, land was pushed up to form the Transantarctic Mountains.

Life in Antarctica

The extreme climate of Antarctica means hardly any life can exist on land. However, the oceans surrounding the continent are full of life-forms. Tiny, shrimplike creatures called krill abound and are eaten by the fish, seals, penguins, and baleen whales that live there. Seals and toothed whales feed on the penguins. No large land-dwelling creatures live on the continent, but a few tiny insects and spiders manage to survive.

Some plant species also survive on Antarctica. Lakes in the Transantarctic Mountains that never freeze completely contain thick mats of tiny organisms. Some lichens grow deep inside rocks in the same region, where they are sheltered from the extreme weather. Some scientists believe they are similar to lichens that have existed and perhaps still exist on Mars.

Exploring Antarctica

The first explorations of Antarctica were carried out by ship. English explorer Captain James Cook (1728–1779) was the first to enter Antarctic waters. He never sighted land, but he did report seeing large numbers of fur seals, which brought seal-hunting ships to the region. Norwegian explorer Carsten Borchgrevink (1864–1934) led the first team to spend winter on the continent.

During the early 1900s, the South Pole became a goal for explorers. In 1909, Irish explorer Ernest Shackleton (1874–1922) tried to reach the Pole but failed. In 1911 a Norwegian expedition led by Roald Amundsen (1872–1928) raced a British team led by Robert Scott (1868–1912) to the Pole. The Norwegians reached their goal on December 14, 1911, beating the British team by a month.

The Antarctic Treaty

By the 1950s, a total of seven countries had laid claim to about 80 percent of Antarctica, based on the achievements of their explorers. In some places, several countries laid claim to the same region, which, it was feared, might lead to war.

To avoid the possibility of war, the United States helped to draw up an agreement called the Antarctic Treaty. The seven nations agreed to suspend their claims to land in Antarctica. The treaty established the continent as a nonmilitary area, open to scientific study by any country. Twelve nations signed in 1959, and the treaty came into effect in 1961. In 1991, Antarctica was made into a natural reserve to protect its wilderness and wildlife.

Mining in the Antarctic

In recent years, several international mining companies have been prospecting (exploring for mineral deposits) in Antarctica. Geologists (scientists who study the structure and history of rocks) believe the continent holds rich deposits of important minerals such as gold, silver, and graphite (carbon) and also has reserves of coal and oil. They base their theories on evidence of minerals found in similar rocks on other continents that were once part of Gondwana.

The original Antarctic Treaty did not cover the issue of mining in Antarctica. In 1991, a new clause was drafted to be added to the treaty. It aimed to ban all mining operations in Antarctica for 50 years. However, not enough nations have yet signed the clause for it to come into effect. Mining remains one of the main threats to the untouched beauty and wildness of Antarctica.

CHECK THESE OUT!
✔CLIMATE ✔CONTINENT ✔EARTH
✔GONDWANA ✔ICE ✔MAGNETIC POLE
✔OZONE LAYER ✔PLATE TECTONICS ✔POLAR REGION

LOOK CLOSER

CFCs and the Ozone Layer

Today, Antarctica holds more than 80 scientific research stations. They are run by many different nations, including Argentina, Australia, Britain, Japan, Russia, and the United States.

Many of the stations are situated on the coast, where the weather is mildest and where they can be resupplied by ship. Some stations are located far inland and can be reached only by specially equipped planes. Many old research stations lie abandoned.

Scientists at the stations include astronomers who study the southern skies, geologists who study the continent's rocks, marine biologists who research life in the oceans, and even psychologists (seye-KAH-luh-jists; scientists who study mind and behavior) who observe the station staff's reactions to life in the Antarctic. The stations are busiest during summer, when the long hours of daylight and milder weather make it easier to get about by plane or snowmobile. Many stations are deserted during the long, dark, and bitterly cold winters.

Apollo Mission

The space program that took people to the Moon in the late 1960s and early 1970s

Astronaut Edwin ("Buzz") Aldrin walks on the surface of the Moon during the **Apollo 11** *extravehicular activity (EVA).*

In 1961 the United States was trailing behind the Soviet Union in the so-called space race. Both superpowers wanted to show the world that they had the technology to put people in space. However, the Soviets were far ahead, launching the first satellite in 1957 and then putting the first person in space in April 1961. The United States was desperate to catch up and launched its first astronaut, Alan Shepard, a month later. On May 25, 1961, President John F. Kennedy made an announcement that grabbed headlines around the world, committing the United States to putting an astronaut on the Moon before the end of the decade. On July 20, 1969, *Apollo 11* touched down in the lunar Sea of Tranquility, and Neil Armstrong became the first person to walk on the surface of the Moon.

HIGHLIGHTS

- The Apollo program allowed the United States to take a lead in the space race for the first time.

- The Apollo spacecraft consisted of three parts—the command module, service module, and lunar module—launched on top of the giant *Saturn V* rocket.

- *Apollo 11* astronauts Neil Armstrong and Buzz Aldrin became the first people on the Moon on July 20, 1969.

- *Apollo 13* nearly ended in disaster after an explosion on board. The astronauts were lucky to return to Earth alive.

- *Apollo 15* through *17* carried a lunar roving vehicle, allowing the astronauts to make longer trips away from their landing site.

Planning and preparation

When Kennedy announced his aim, the National Aeronautics and Space Administration (NASA) was at the very beginning of its crewed space flight program—it had not even managed to put an astronaut into orbit. NASA had to work fast on two different fronts, continuing to gain

Race for the Moon

For years, the Soviet Union denied they had ever planned to send cosmonauts to the Moon. (*Cosmonaut* is the Russian term for astronaut.) They always kept their space program secret. The truth is that they did have plans but ran into difficulties and never caught up. The first Soviet plan, devised by 1964, would have used three separate spacecraft called the Soyuz complex. The first stage was to launch a large uncrewed rocket into orbit with hardly any fuel on board. Then, several tanker spacecraft would be sent up to fuel the rocket in orbit, followed by a crewed lunar spacecraft that would link up with the rocket and fly to the Moon. This plan was scrapped at the end of 1964. By 1968, a new Soviet spacecraft, the Zond, was being tested for a lunar expedition. After early successes, NASA was worried that the Soviets might try to get ahead by sending astronauts to orbit the Moon in late 1968. NASA stepped up the schedule of *Apollo 8* to beat them to it. Shortly after this, the Zond program ran into problems with its booster rockets, and by the time these had been resolved, *Apollo 11* had landed on the Moon. The race was over.

astronaut experience with its Mercury program and learning more about the Moon with a series of robot surveyors and landers. A lunar mission would be enormously difficult. The planners also had to develop a complex mission profile involving a three-part spacecraft that would separate and link together again in lunar orbit. The Gemini missions, which followed the Mercury program, were designed to give astronauts and engineers experience with these complex operations before they would be pushed to the limit by Apollo.

NASA also needed to develop a new launch vehicle to blast the spacecraft toward the Moon. In the early 1960s, the most powerful rockets were capable only of putting satellites and space capsules into a low orbit, around 248 miles (400 km) above Earth. Launching an Apollo spacecraft to the Moon would require much more power. NASA engineers, led by German-born rocket pioneer Wernher von Braun (1912–1977), began to design the Saturn V, a vast three-stage rocket over 364 feet (111 m) tall.

The Apollo spacecraft

The Apollo spacecraft was made of three different modules: the command module, the service module, and the lunar module. Each part had its own role to play in the overall mission.

The astronauts spent most of the flight to and from the Moon inside the command module. This cone-shaped structure had a heat shield at its base, and was the only part of the Apollo spacecraft to return to Earth at the end of a mission. It also contained all the vital controls necessary for maneuvering the spacecraft.

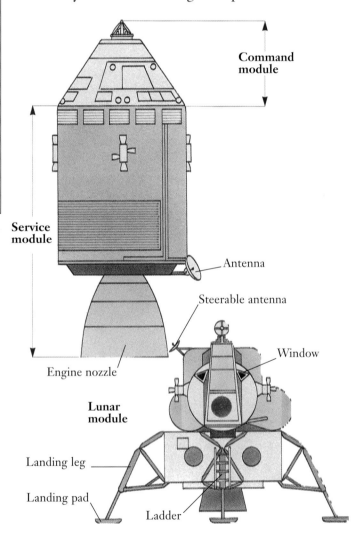

Each Apollo spacecraft consisted of three main modules: the command module, the service module, and the lunar module that landed on the Moon.

The service module was a cylinder-shaped unit with a rocket engine on the base. It contained all the life-support systems needed during the long flight and the rocket propellant. Its main functions were to slow the spacecraft when it reached the Moon and later to provide the boost needed to escape lunar orbit and return to Earth.

The lunar module was a spidery spacecraft—with several stiltlike legs—in which two of Apollo's three astronauts traveled down to the Moon's surface. It also contained a rocket engine. When ready to return to lunar orbit, the bottom half of the lunar module was blasted away and left on the Moon.

Mission profile

At launch, the command module and service module were joined together at the very top of the Saturn V rocket. The lunar module was packed into a protective shell below the other two parts. By the time the spacecraft left Earth's orbit, most of the rocket stages had fallen away. The command and service modules had to separate from the remaining upper stage and turn around in midflight so that the lunar module could be docked to a hatch on top of the command module. Apollo arrived in lunar orbit flying backward so that the service module engines could fire and slow down the spacecraft.

The Apollo missions had a crew of three: two astronauts in the lunar module and one in the command module. One of the command module astronauts described himself as "the loneliest man alive." While he remained in orbit, the lunar module separated and fell toward the Moon's surface, slowing itself down by firing its engine as a retrorocket, that is, using its thrust to slow the module as it approached the lunar surface.

At the end of the mission, the top half of the lunar module blasted off from the Moon's surface and rejoined the command and service modules. Once the astronauts and their equipment were safely back on the command module, the lunar module was dumped onto the surface of the Moon. Another firing of the service module's engines put the spacecraft on a return path to

The historic **Apollo 11** *lunar-landing mission ends with the successful return of astronauts Neil Armstrong, Michael Collins, and "Buzz" Aldrin.*

Earth's orbit. The command module separated from the service module and dropped back through the atmosphere, using parachutes to slow it down before splashing into the ocean.

Early Apollo missions

For a program that had been so carefully planned in advance, Apollo had a disastrous start. During a launch rehearsal in January 1967, astronauts Virgil Grissom, Roger Chaffee, and Edward White were killed by an electrical fire that broke out in the command module. After this disaster, later named *Apollo 1*, the entire program was halted for 10 months while the spacecraft design was changed to make it safer. In particular, the highly explosive pure oxygen atmosphere in the command module was replaced by a mixture more like normal air.

After a series of uncrewed test flights, the first successful crewed Apollo mission was *Apollo 7*, launched on October 11, 1968. This mission was designed to test the performance of the command module over long periods of time. It remained in orbit around Earth for 10 days—the same amount of time the full mission would take.

Apollo 8 was the first crewed mission to go beyond Earth's orbit. Until this time, the record altitude reached by an astronaut was 850 miles (1,370 km), set during the 1966 flight of

Gemini 11. Apollo 8, by contrast, crossed nearly 250,000 miles (400,000 km) to reach lunar orbit and made 10 circuits of the Moon before returning to Earth. For the first time, astronauts were able to describe and photograph Earth from a distance. This had a huge effect on public awareness of Earth's smallness and fragility.

NASA's policy was to rehearse the mission one step at a time. The next stage was to rehearse the complicated docking with the lunar module using *Apollo 9* in Earth's orbit. *Apollo 10* then carried out a full rehearsal, flying to the Moon and simulating a landing by the lunar module.

Apollo 11

Because of the success of *Apollo 7* through *10*, *Apollo 11* was given the go-ahead to make a lunar landing. The crew of Neil Armstrong, Michael Collins, and Edwin "Buzz" Aldrin launched from Kennedy Space Center in Florida on July 16, 1969, and reached the Moon three days later. Aldrin and Armstrong boarded the lunar module, leaving Collins in the command module. NASA had selected the Sea of Tranquility (an enormous plain that was once flooded by lava) as a good landing site, and Armstrong had to guide the spacecraft in manually.

Once safely on the Moon, the astronauts put on their spacesuits and went out onto the surface for an extravehicular activity (EVA). Armstrong was chosen to be the first person on the Moon. On July 20, 1969, he climbed down the ladder to the surface, with the words, "That's one small step for man, a giant leap for mankind." A quarter of the world's population watched or listened to the moment on television and radio.

Once Armstrong had gotten used to moving around in his spacesuit in one-sixth gravity, Aldrin joined him on the surface. Their EVA lasted two-and-a-half hours, as they collected rock samples, photographed and described the scenery, and performed other experiments. After spending the night in the lunar module, they left the Moon the following day, linking up with Collins in orbit before returning to Earth. After splashdown, the three astronauts were kept in isolation for several weeks in case they had picked up any dangerous microorganisms while on the Moon. When cleared, they were taken on a triumphant tour of the United States, including a ticker-tape parade through New York City.

Apollo 12

The next Apollo mission followed in November 1969. This time, astronauts Charles Conrad and Alan Bean set their lunar module down in a region called the Ocean of Storms, within a few hundred feet of a much earlier robot probe, *Surveyor 3*. One aim of the mission was to take parts of *Surveyor* back to Earth for NASA's scientists to see how it had stood up to more than two years on the Moon. The astronauts made two EVAs during the mission, setting up more experiments, collecting rock samples, and taking more photographs. The mission was hailed as a complete success.

Apollo 13

Just as NASA was making travel to the Moon look easy, *Apollo 13*'s mission in April 1970 went disastrously wrong. Its astronaut crew were lucky to return to Earth alive because a short-circuit and explosion in the service module crippled the life-support systems in the command module when the spacecraft was already on its way to the Moon. James Lovell, John Swigert, and

Fred Haise had no choice but to climb into the lunar module and seal it off from the rest of their spacecraft. The only option was to continue to the Moon, swing around it, and then head back to Earth. The three astronauts had to survive for three-and-a-half days in a lunar module built to support two astronauts for two days. However, with the help of engineers back at Mission Control, they managed to overcome huge problems, including near-freezing temperatures, a build-up of dangerous carbon dioxide, and a shortage of electrical power. As they returned to Earth, the astronauts had to face the biggest danger of all—reactivating the command module and reentering Earth's atmosphere with most of their instruments out of order. They managed it safely and returned to a hero's welcome.

Later Apollo missions

After the near-disaster of *Apollo 13*, the Moon program was suspended again while NASA reviewed safety and redesigned several of the systems. *Apollo 14* launched in January 1971 and was a complete success. The later Apollo missions (*15*, *16*, and *17*) were even more ambitious than the program so far. The lunar module carried a car called the lunar roving vehicle. The astronauts spent much longer

This container has lunar surface material inside, collected during the **Apollo 11** *mission.*

LOOK CLOSER

Lunar Vehicles

The final three Apollo missions carried a two-person buggy called the lunar roving vehicle (LRV). This allowed the astronauts to travel for much longer distances and to collect samples from a wider range of lunar surfaces. The lunar module team on *Apollo 17*, for instance, traveled over 35 km (22 miles).

The LRV was 10 feet (3 m) long and 6½ feet (2 m) wide, built around an aluminum framework. It had four wheels, each with a separate electric motor, and a cruising speed of 8½ miles per hour (14 km/h). To withstand the shock of traveling over the bumpy lunar surface in low gravity, the wheels were made of woven wire mesh with rubber treads on the edges. The vehicle also had a gyroscopic compass for navigation (since the Moon has no magnetic field, a normal compass would be useless) and an umbrella-shaped antenna for communication with Earth. Commander Eugene Cernan of *Apollo 17* called the LRV "the finest machine I have ever had the pleasure to drive."

outside the spacecraft carrying out more complex experiments. There was still time for some fun, though—one astronaut even played golf on the Moon.

On Earth, however, questions were being asked about the cost of the Apollo program, and the public was losing interest. NASA wanted to concentrate on developing its reusable space shuttle and was also faced with budget cuts. The final Apollo missions were cancelled, and the last astronauts on the Moon left in December 1972. The last Apollo mission was a linkup with a Soviet Soyuz space capsule in orbit around Earth in 1975. However the science stations set up on the Moon continued to return information until they were switched off in 1977. The Apollo missions are still humanity's most ambitious venture into space, but there are no plans for people to return to the Moon in the near future.

CHECK THESE OUT!
✔GEMINI MISSION ✔LUNAR MISSION
✔MERCURY MISSION ✔RUSSIAN SPACE MISSION

Arctic Ocean

**The smallest of the world's oceans,
covering the northernmost region of Earth**

The northern cap of Earth around the North Pole is covered by the Arctic Ocean. The Arctic is the smallest of Earth's oceans, at only about one-seventh the size of the Atlantic. It stretches over about 5.4 million square miles (13,986,000 sq km) between the north coasts of Canada and Eurasia.

Unlike other oceans, the Arctic is largely enclosed by land and shallow seas. On the Eurasian side of the ocean, north of Russia, there is a very wide continental shelf (margin of continents that lies between the shoreline and shelf slope). This shelf is covered by several shallow seas, including the Barents, Kara, Laptev, East Siberian, and Chukchi Seas.

The central part of the Arctic Ocean is about 2½ miles (4 km) deep. This is close to the average depth of all the world's oceans. However, because the shallow seas make up nearly 37 percent of the Arctic Ocean, the average depth of this ocean is only 4,300 feet (1,312 m), making it the shallowest ocean on Earth.

HIGHLIGHTS

◆ The Arctic Ocean is the smallest and shallowest of Earth's oceans, stretching over the North Pole between Canada and Eurasia.

◆ Around 50 percent of the Arctic Ocean is covered by permanent ice, which varies in thickness according to the season.

◆ The ocean floor consists of two deep basins, each divided into two by underwater ridges.

◆ There is a layer of warmer water below the very cold surface water of the Arctic Ocean. It has a high salt content so it is denser and does not rise.

An Arctic survey ship makes its way through huge ice floes off the coast of Spitsbergen.

Scientists once thought the Arctic Ocean was a single large basin, however, explorations during the 1950s revealed the ocean floor had two deep basins divided by the Lomonosov Ridge, stretching 1,100 miles (1,770 km) from Ellesmere Island between Canada and Greenland to the New Siberian Islands. Each basin is also divided by a smaller ridge.

Nearly half of the Arctic Ocean is covered by a cap of permanent ice about 10 to 11½ feet (3 to 3.5 m) thick in winter, thinning to 8 feet (2.4 m) in summer. The ice often reaches the shore in winter, especially in the Siberian seas. The ice pack is constantly broken into huge floes (flat masses of floating ice) by the wind and currents.

Although the surface waters of the ocean are very cold, there is a layer of warmer water at a depth of 600 to 3,000 feet (183 to 915 m). This water does not rise to the surface. Its high salt content makes it denser than the surface water.

The solid ice cap means the waters of the Arctic Ocean are generally calm and the sea currents are weak. This cap is slowly carried in a clockwise direction by the currents, around 5,700 to 8,600 feet (1,739 to 2,623 m) per day. Water takes two to three years to cross the Arctic Ocean. Surface water flows out between Greenland and Spitsbergen, carrying ice floes south into the Atlantic and icebergs carved off Greenland glaciers. Warm Atlantic water flows from the other side of Spitsbergen into the Barents Sea, then northeast into the Kara Sea, keeping the Norwegian coast free of ice.

Resources

So far the Arctic region has not been greatly exploited for economic purposes, and many feel that things should stay this way. However, scientists think the region contains many resources. It is one of the world's most important sources of oil and natural gas. Most of the drilling takes place offshore. Around the ice

---

DISCOVERERS

William Barents

For many years, geographers were convinced there were sea passages north of the coasts of Russia and Canada. These passages would be useful for trade between Europe and the East because they would be much shorter than sailing around the tip of South America and Africa. Many explorers set out to discover the passages. Dutch explorer William Barents (around 1550–1597) made three voyages searching for a northeast passage from the north Atlantic to the Pacific. The Barents Sea between Spitsbergen and northern Russia is named for the explorer. Barents's report that the seas were full of whales, walruses, and seals started many large-scale fishing industries.

On his third voyage, Barents became the first to sail as far as 80 degrees north latitude. Knowing that the Kara Strait was often blocked by ice floes, he sailed farther north, discovering Bear Island and Spitsbergen. The expedition continued eastward, but Barents's ship was crushed by ice. He and his crew survived the winter in a cabin built from the ship's timbers. In spring they set off southward in their remaining boats. After a harrowing 1,600-mile (2,574-km) journey, the expedition reached the Kola Peninsula in Russia. Barents, however, died from the cold after leaving the cabin.

---

cap are rich fishing grounds producing more than 10 percent of the world's catch. The most important renewable source in the Arctic is fresh water. Some of the world's largest rivers flow into the ocean, including the Mackenzie River in Canada and the Lena in Russia. These rivers—or part of them—could be diverted to other regions that are short of water. The water could also be used to produce electricity. However, these activities would change the Artic's environment.

In summer the open waterways close to land are used for transportation. North of Russia, convoys of ships escorted by icebreakers carry raw materials from Siberia west as far as Japan.

CHECK THESE OUT!
✔CONTINENTAL SHELF ✔GLACIER ✔ICE ✔OCEAN

Asteroid

A small rocky body in orbit around the Sun

As well as the Sun, the nine planets, and their moons, the Solar System (the group of objects that revolve around the Sun) is full of smaller objects. Some of these are icy comets and many are asteroids (minor planets). Most asteroids are just small lumps of rock, but a few are several hundred miles wide. Asteroids are confined mostly to the asteroid belt between the orbits of Mars and Jupiter, but a few come close to Earth and sometimes even collide with it.

What is an asteroid?

Asteroids and comets (lumps of ice and rock) are the bits left over after the Solar System was created 4.6 billion years ago. As the planets were forming, they swept up most of the interstellar (between the stars) dust and gas that was orbiting the Sun, but not all of it. In places, the planets were not close enough to pull in the debris (duh-BREE; broken pieces). Over millions of years, the dust particles collided and stuck together at random, but only a few got big enough to have noticeable gravity and pull in their neighbors.

HIGHLIGHTS

◆ Asteroids are the debris left over from the formation of the Solar System.

◆ Asteroids regularly crash into Earth—one may have killed off the dinosaurs 66.4 million years ago.

Astronomers (scientists who study planets and stars) think asteroids are a sort of deep-frozen record of the material in the early Solar System.

Most asteroids seem to be small, oddly shaped lumps of rock. Photographs sent back by space probes show they are pitted with craters from collisions during their formation. Only the very largest, such as Ceres and Pallas, had enough gravity to pull themselves into a sphere (ball shape).

A diagram showing the orbits of some asteroids found inside the asteroid belt or closer to Earth.

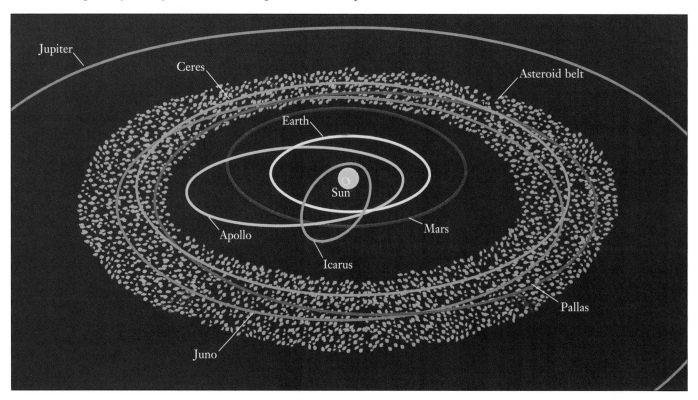

Astronomers get most of their knowledge about asteroids from analyzing the sunlight reflected by them and by comparing them with meteorites (MEE-tee-uh-RYTS; lumps of rock that reach Earth from outer space) that occasionally crash into Earth. Most asteroids are very dark, which may mean they have frost or dark organic (carbon- and hydrogen-containing) compounds on their surfaces. Most seem to be made of rock, but at least some contain large amounts of iron and nickel with a thin coating of rocky minerals called regolith (REG-uh-lith).

Asteroid belts

Most of the asteroids in the Solar System are confined within a few distinct belts. The best-known and most crowded is the belt between Mars and Jupiter. Ceres, Pallas, Juno, and Vesta were the very first asteroids to be discovered here from 1801 onward by Italian Giuseppe Piazzi and a team of astronomers around the world who called themselves the "space police." At the time Ceres was discovered, Piazzi was looking for a new planet between Mars and Jupiter. According to theories at the time, there was an obvious gap in the Solar System at this point. Thousands of asteroids have now been discovered. Astronomers think up to 10 billion others are still unknown. Even when lumped together, they could not make up a planet the size of Mercury. Asteroids are not a hazard to space missions. They are so far apart that the belt is mostly empty space.

The other two major groups of asteroids in the Solar System are the Trojans (TROH-juhnz) and the Kuiper (KOY-per) Belt. The Trojans go around the Sun in the same orbit as Jupiter. They are held there by an effect of Jupiter's enormous gravity. The Kuiper Belt has only been discovered in the past few years, as it lies out in the depths of the Solar System. Astronomers are still unsure as to whether these objects are officially asteroids or dormant comets.

Not all asteroids stay in the main circular belts around the Sun. Some groups have highly elliptical (ih-LIP-tih-kuhl) orbits, which take them close to the Sun at one point and farther into space at the other extreme. The major group of these are the near-Earth asteroids, with orbits that cross or come close to Earth's own.

LOOK CLOSER

Risk of Collision

Astronomers think there could be as many as 330,000 medium-sized asteroids in orbits that come near Earth, so it is only a matter of time before there is a collision. Several collisions have happened in the past and may have been important in the development of life on Earth. Many scientists think that an asteroid that crashed into the Gulf of Mexico 66.4 million years ago was responsible for the extinction of the dinosaurs.

Probes to the asteroids

The first idea of what an asteroid looked like came from the Viking Mars probes of the 1970s. These probes photographed Mars's moons Phobos and Deimos (DY-muhs), which were thought to be asteroids that were captured in the gravitational field of the planet. More recently, the Galileo space probe flew past and photographed the asteroids Ida and Gaspra on its way to Jupiter.

The first dedicated asteroid probe was the NEAR (Near-Earth Asteroid Rendezvous), which successfully landed on the asteroid Eros on February 12, 2001. NEAR was designed to investigate the composition of asteroids in more detail. Some space scientists and businesspeople hope to mine asteroids in the near future to provide huge amounts of iron, nickel, and precious metals.

CHECK THESE OUT!
✔COMET ✔EXTINCTION ✔METEOR ✔SOLAR SYSTEM

Astronomy

The study of the Universe and the matter it contains

Astronomy is the oldest science—it began when humans first looked at the sky and wondered about the objects they saw there. At first, they used the regular cycles of movement purely for measuring time, but they were also fascinated by what these objects were, and this gave rise to myths, legends, and practical theories about the Universe. Today, astronomers use huge telescopes and powerful computers to answer some of the biggest questions about the past and future of the cosmos (the Universe).

Early astronomy

Archeological sites around the world show that ancient peoples had a good understanding of the objects and cycles they saw in the sky, even before they invented writing. Monuments as far apart as Stonehenge in England and the Temple of Karnak in Egypt are aligned to sunrises and sunsets at important times of the year. The ancient Egyptians also used the annual movement of the Sun against the background stars to predict the flooding of the River Nile.

However, the real birthplace of scientific astronomy is probably Mesopotamia (part of modern Iraq). Around the 5th century B.C.E.,

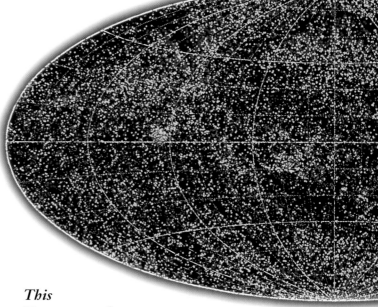

This X-ray map of the sky shows 50,000 X-ray sources and was obtained by satellite.

astronomers were drawing star maps, creating constellation patterns in the sky, and predicting the paths of the Sun, Moon, and planets. Their main reason for doing this was astrology (attempting to predict the future from the movements of the stars), but their methods were scientific. In fact, astronomy and astrology were one and the same until just a few centuries ago.

Greek astronomers and philosophers created some of the first theories of the Universe based on observation. Most put Earth (which they knew was round) at the center, with the Sun, Moon, planets, and stars moving around it, but a man called Aristarchus of Samos (around 270 B.C.E.) discovered that the Sun was larger than Earth. He therefore realized that the Sun should be at the center. However, religious teachings and apparent common sense (if the Earth is moving, why can its movement not be felt?) meant that his ideas did not catch on.

One major problem for early astronomy was the belief, passed down from Greek philosophers, that everything in the Universe had to move in perfect circles. This caused major difficulties in understanding the movement of the planets, which occasionally slow down, speed up, or even

HIGHLIGHTS

- ◆ Astronomy is the study of the Universe.

- ◆ Modern astronomy uses space probes, powerful telescopes, and supercomputers to understand the planets, stars, and the Universe itself.

- ◆ The most important revolution in astronomy came when people realized Earth moved around the Sun, and not the other way around.

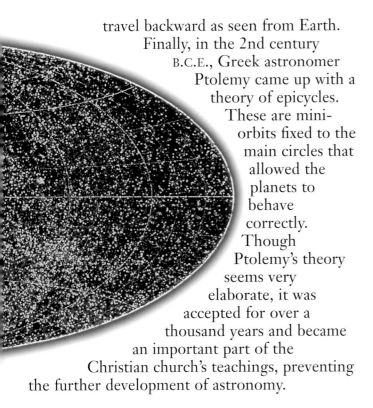

travel backward as seen from Earth. Finally, in the 2nd century B.C.E., Greek astronomer Ptolemy came up with a theory of epicycles. These are mini-orbits fixed to the main circles that allowed the planets to behave correctly. Though Ptolemy's theory seems very elaborate, it was accepted for over a thousand years and became an important part of the Christian church's teachings, preventing the further development of astronomy.

Figuring out the Universe

In the 15th century, things finally began to change. A revival of learning, arts, and sciences called the Renaissance swept across Europe, and people began to question the accepted wisdom passed down from Greek and Roman times.

In 1543, a Polish priest, Nicolaus Copernicus (1473–1543), produced a new theory of the Universe with the Sun at the center and Earth in orbit around it. However, Copernicus's Universe

DISCOVERERS

Brahe and Kepler

Tycho Brahe (1546–1601) was a Danish astronomer who worked with his sister Sofie Brahe (around 1556–1643). Tycho Brahe worked before the invention of the telescope, but he still developed measuring instruments that allowed him to make the most accurate tables of the movements of planets. Although he did not believe in the Copernican idea of a Sun-centered Solar System, his measurements were later used by his student Johannes Kepler (1571–1630), who proved that the Copernican model could work. Kepler's three laws of planetary motion explained that the planets moved in ellipses rather than circles, that they moved faster closer to the Sun, and that the time they take to orbit the Sun depends on their average distance from it.

was flawed because he too believed the planets had circular orbits. His theory worked no better than Ptolemy's and was easily ignored.

The great revolution in astronomy came in the 1600s. The principle of the telescope was discovered around 1608 by a Dutch lensmaker. Within a year, astronomers across Europe were using their own instruments to look at the sky.

The most important and controversial observations were made by Italian scientist Galileo Galilei (1564–1642). He sketched sunspots covering the supposedly perfect face of the Sun, found that the Milky Way was made up of countless faint stars, that the planet Jupiter has four moons, and that the planet Venus shows phases like our own Moon as different parts of it face the Sun. The moons of Jupiter proved that not everything in the Universe revolved around Earth, and the phases of Venus showed that it had to be orbiting the Sun closer than Earth. Galileo's announcement of these discoveries and his insistence on teaching a Sun-centered model of the Universe led him into conflict with the Church, but the new ideas spread, and astronomy started to develop rapidly.

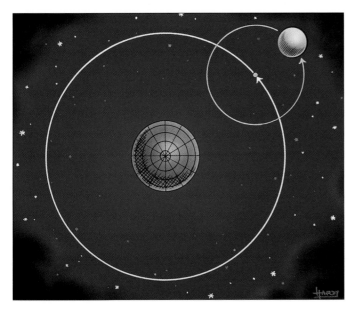

The Ptolemaic system placed Earth at the center of the Universe, with every other body orbiting it.

Understanding orbits

The movement of the planets was still a problem to be solved. The solution came from the careful observations of Danish astronomer Tycho Brahe (1546–1601), his sister, astronomer and alchemist Sofie Brahe (around 1556–1643), and their student Johannes Kepler (1571–1630). Kepler proved that the movements of all the planets made sense if they orbited the Sun in stretched elliptical (oval) orbits rather than perfect circles.

Still, no one knew what kept the planets in their orbits. The ancients thought the planets were fixed to the inside of invisible spheres, but the Brahes' observations showed comets move in orbits that cut through the spheres without any effect—proving the spheres were not there at all. English physicist Isaac Newton (1642–1727) finally found the answer, and he explained gravity in his 1687 book, the *Principia Mathematica*.

Expanding Universe

Having solved the mysteries of the Solar System, astronomers now turned their attention to what lay beyond. For example, how far away are the stars? The whole question of measuring distances in the vastness of space was a difficult one. Kepler's laws could be used inside the Solar System, but beyond it astronomers had to build up a wide range of techniques.

In this image of the Canada-France-Hawaii telescope, circular star trails are seen in the sky.

The first was measurement by parallax. This is the effect that makes nearby objects seem to move against background objects when the point of view changes slightly. This is easily demonstrated by holding out a finger at arm's length against a distant background and looking at it through one eye, and then the other. By measuring the angle by which an object shifts against the background, it is possible to calculate its distance if the separation between the two points of view is known. Astronomers used this principle by observing stars from opposite sides of Earth's orbit—six months and 190 million miles (300 million km) apart—and measuring their shifts against the background. From this, they discovered that the stars were immensely distant, so far away that today their distances are measured in light-years.

The vast distances to the stars led astronomers to realize that they were actually distant suns. Parallax measurements revealed that some must be much brighter than the Sun, but the wide range of colors they displayed were a mystery.

Some of the most important breakthroughs around this time came from British Astronomer Royal, William Herschel (1738–1822), assisted by his sister Caroline Herschel (1750–1848). In 1781 he had discovered Uranus, a new planet in the outer Solar System, but was also fascinated by some of the bigger questions. While analyzing

STORY OF SCIENCE

Newton's Laws

Isaac Newton (1642–1727) realized there was some sort of force that pulled objects together. He thought the same force, gravity, was responsible for keeping the Moon in orbit around Earth or causing an apple to fall to the ground. He developed his ideas into four laws. The fourth of these—his law of gravitation—describes how the force of gravity between two objects increases if the mass of either object increases, and decreases rapidly as the distance between the objects decreases. Although his laws do not provide a good description of the behavior of the smallest particles or of objects moving near the speed of light, they describe the behavior of objects in all but the most extreme situations.

sunlight split into a rainbow spectrum through a prism (PRIH-zuhm; a transparent body that separates the different colors in light), he discovered invisible infrared (heat) radiation, opening the way for modern astronomy, which looks at a wide range of different radiations. Herschel was also the first astronomer to suggest that the Sun, all the stars in the sky, and the Milky Way were part of a huge, disk-shaped star system, which he called the galaxy.

In the 19th century, astronomers used photography to record images of the Sun, Moon, and stars. German scientist Joseph von Fraunhofer (1787–1826) had discovered dark lines crossing the spectrum of light from the Sun. He realized they were caused by elements in the Sun's atmosphere absorbing light. These lines are termed spectra. Photography allowed astronomers to record the spectra of faint stars, and work began to classify the stars into a sequence according to their color and the elements within them. This eventually resulted in the Hertzsprung–Russell diagram, which shows how the brightness of a star depends on its color, mass, and the stage in its life cycle. With this information, astronomers could work out the distance to almost any star in the galaxy and could begin to work out how stars shine.

Cepheid variables

Another important method of finding distances in the Universe uses Cepheid (SEH-fee-id) variables—stars that change their brightness in a regular cycle. The length of this cycle depends on the star's average brightness, so if astronomers work out the length of the cycle, they can find the star's brightness and therefore its distance.

Edwin Hubble used Cepheid variables to measure the distance of some of the faint spiral nebulas in the sky, discovering that they were millions of light-years away in separate galaxies. He also discovered that the dark lines in the spectra of these galaxies were slightly shifted toward the red end of the spectrum. This red shift, caused by the Doppler effect, shows that other galaxies are moving away from us. Hubble found that the farther away the galaxy was, the bigger the red shift. This could only mean one thing: the Universe is expanding.

Astronomy today

Although astronomers argued fiercely about the meaning of Hubble's discovery, nearly all now agree that the Universe is rushing outward from a huge explosion—the big bang—which created the Universe around 12 billion years ago.

Thanks to astronomy, more is known about the Universe than ever before. Space probes have provided close-up views of all the planets except Pluto. Astronomers today use giant telescopes in space and on the ground. Because of the length of time that light from distant objects takes to reach Earth, astronomers can look back in time.

The full range of the electromagnetic spectrum can also be used to look at objects much cooler or hotter than those that shine in visible light. However, there are still questions to be answered. Astronomers still do not understand exactly what happened in the big bang, how the galaxies formed, whether there is life elsewhere in the Universe, and what the Universe's ultimate fate will be. Astronomers hope to answer these questions in the near future.

CHECK THESE OUT!
✔DOPPLER EFFECT ✔STAR ✔SUN ✔UNIVERSE

Atlantic Ocean

The second largest of Earth's four main oceans

The Atlantic Ocean is second only to the Pacific Ocean in size. It covers 31,862,000 square miles (82,500,000 sq km)—about one-sixth of Earth's surface. It is bounded by North and South America in the west and by Europe and Africa in the east. The icy continent of Antarctica lies to the south, with Greenland and the Labrador, Norwegian, and Greenland Seas to the north. The equator (ih-KWAY-tuhr; an imaginary circle around Earth at equal distances from the North and South Poles) divides this vast ocean into the North and South Atlantic, each having its own currents.

The ocean bed

On average the Atlantic Ocean is 12,257 feet (3,736 m) deep. However, the seabed is by no means flat. The Mid-Atlantic Ridge is an undersea mountain chain that runs north-south along the center of the ocean floor for its entire length. In places, the ridge towers more than

Covering one-sixth of Earth's surface, the Atlantic Ocean is bounded by the continents of Europe and Africa on the east and by the Americas on the west.

16,400 feet (5,000 m) above the surrounding ocean plain. It breaks the ocean's surface to form the large island of Iceland and several smaller island groups such as the Azores (AY-ZOHRZ).

Once the Atlantic region was accurately mapped, geographers noticed that the landmasses forming its western and eastern borders seem to fit together like pieces in a jigsaw puzzle. When rocks from the ocean floor were brought to the surface, scientists found they were young and newly formed. They questioned whether these discoveries could help explain the ocean's origins.

In the 1960s, the theory of plate tectonics provided an answer to the riddle of the ocean's origin. According to this theory, Earth's crust and part of the upper mantle (outer layer) is not

HIGHLIGHTS

◆ The Atlantic Ocean is bounded by the continents of Europe and Africa to the east, by the Americas to the west, by Antarctica to the south, and by Greenland and the icy polar seas that surround it to the north.

◆ The equator divides the ocean into the North Atlantic and the South Atlantic. Each area has its own patterns of circulation (ocean currents).

◆ Waters near the ocean surface circulate in different patterns from those in the ocean depths.

LOOK CLOSER

Industries of the Atlantic

Fishing is a very important industry in the Atlantic Ocean. In the mid-1990s, Atlantic fishing accounted for about a quarter of the world's total catch. This figure was much lower than in previous years. In past centuries, the Grand Banks off Newfoundland were one of the world's richest fishing grounds. Recently, however, overfishing in the region has severely reduced stocks of fish. The South Atlantic is an important source of tuna, hake, and herring. The North Atlantic holds stocks of cod and herring.

In the Atlantic, the rocks below the shallow seas off the coasts of continents, called continental shelves, are rich in minerals and petroleum. For example, coal and natural gas are found in the continental shelf off Britain, diamonds are mined on the southwestern shelf of Africa, and the west coast of Africa has rich oil and natural gas deposits.

The Atlantic is an important source of fish, but overfishing is reducing the numbers of tuna, hake, herring, and cod.

continuous but is made up of large plates. The plates float on the lower part of the mantle, the layer below, and drift very slowly, colliding or rubbing against one another, or pulling apart.

Around 200 million years ago, scientists believed that all the continents were joined together to form one giant supercontinent called Pangaea (pan-JEE-uh). Very slowly, in the course of the next 110 million years, the plates moved to open up a rift (crack) in Pangaea. North America slowly separated from North Africa and Europe, and the Atlantic Ocean formed. Later, South America and Africa drifted apart. The Mid-Atlantic Ridge formed along the rift itself.

As the plates on either side of the crack drifted apart, lava (LAH-vuh; molten rock) from deep inside Earth welled up. As it met the water, the lava cooled to form a new seabed made of the rock basalt (buh-SAWLT). Scientists have discovered that the ocean is growing wider by about ½ to ¾ inch (1 to 2 cm) each year. The rift itself forms a narrow cleft between 9 and 31 miles (15 and 50 km) wide and from 3,280 to 6,560 feet (1,000 to 2,000 m) deep.

Atlantic seas

Several smaller seas edge the North Atlantic. The Mediterranean, North, and Baltic Seas lie to the east, with the Norwegian and Greenland Seas in the north. To the west lie the Gulf of Mexico, the Caribbean Sea, and the Labrador Sea, which is directly connected to the Atlantic Ocean. In the South Atlantic, the Scotia and Weddell Seas lie close to Antarctica.

The Sargasso Sea is a body of warm, still water. It has weak currents and lies near the center of the North Atlantic, miles away from any land. It is named after the sargassum weed that grows at its surface. This region experiences low rainfall and light winds.

Ocean currents

The waters of the North and South Atlantic flow separately in large gyres (JIH-ers; roughly circular patterns), which rarely mix together. The waters rotate clockwise in the Northern Hemisphere and counterclockwise in the Southern Hemisphere. The circulation is driven by strong easterly winds called trade winds just north and south of the equator. Warm water is driven westward, forming the north and south equatorial currents.

The warm waters of the tropical Atlantic are a breeding ground for hurricanes in summer. As warm, moist air rises in the region, water vapor condenses to form rain, which releases heat. These events create low-pressure centers that can grow into hurricanes.

The rotation of Earth increases the force of currents flowing on the western side of the gyres. Along the western boundaries of the Atlantic, the water flows at speeds of more than 6½ feet per second (2 m/s), within a narrow band measuring about 62 miles (100 km) across. In the North Atlantic, the powerful Gulf Stream flows northeastward from Florida along the northeast coast of North America. The cold Labrador Current flows from northern waters in roughly the opposite direction to meet the Gulf Stream off Newfoundland. In the South Atlantic, the weaker Brazil Current flows southward.

On the eastern side of the Atlantic, slower currents flow at speeds of around 9½ inches per second (25 cm/s) over a much wider area, measuring about 620 miles (1,000 km) across. These eastern currents are linked with the upwelling of cold, mineral-rich waters along the coast of West Africa. Along the southern edge of the Atlantic, the cold Antarctic Circumpolar

A drilling platform in the shallow waters of a continental shelf in the Atlantic. These shelf rocks contain rich deposits of natural gas and oil.

Current flows eastward around Antarctica. Driven by high-level westerly winds, this current helps the waters of the Atlantic, Pacific, and Indian Oceans to circulate and mix.

Deep ocean currents

While the wind drives the circulation of waters near the ocean's surface, water in the ocean depths circulates in different ways. Here, currents are driven by differences in density between masses of water. Dense water tends to sink below less dense water.

In the Atlantic, as in several other oceans, different masses of water have different temperatures and vary in the levels of salt and oxygen that they contain. The high salt content of the Mediterranean Sea makes the water so dense that it sinks to depths of 3,300 to 6,600 feet (1,000 to 2,000 m) after flowing through the Straits of Gibraltar. In the South Atlantic, the waters of the Antarctic Circumpolar Current are also dense. These waters sink as they flow into the North Atlantic.

The water in the ocean depths is called bottom water. In the Atlantic, bottom water originates either in the Labrador Sea situated in the far north or in the Weddell Sea situated off Antarctica in the far south. In the North Atlantic, deep water is formed when very salty water flowing northward to the Labrador and Greenland Seas meets and mixes with very cold water that is less salty, flowing from the Arctic Ocean. This huge mass of deep water is much greater than the bottom water of the South Atlantic. It drives most of the deep-water circulation of the world's oceans.

Bottom water circulates very slowly through the ocean depths, taking as long as 1,000 years to complete one circuit of the world's oceans. This slow circulation helps to maintain levels of oxygen dissolved in the ocean depths, and so helps to sustain life in the deep sea. Some scientists believe that deep-water circulation also has a major influence on the world's climate, affecting, for example, the timing of ice ages.

CHECK THESE OUT!
✔CONTINENTAL SHELF ✔EARTH
✔OCEAN CURRENT ✔PANGAEA ✔PLATE TECTONICS

Atmosphere

**An envelope of gas that surrounds Earth
and other planets of the Solar System**

It is Earth's atmosphere that allows life to
survive. Without the protection of the
atmosphere, Earth would be poisoned by cosmic
radiation, bombarded by meteors, and exposed
to extremes of hot and cold temperatures.

The atmosphere is an envelope of layers of
gases, liquids, and particles, up to 250 miles (400
km) thick around the planet. It is held in place by
Earth's gravity (the force of attraction between
all objects in the Universe), so it is most dense
near the surface and gradually becomes thinner
with increasing altitude (AL-tuh-TYOOD; the
height of the land above sea level).

Winds in the lower levels of the atmosphere
spread out the heat from the Sun and produce
acceptable temperatures around the globe.
Higher up, molecules (MAH-lih-KYOOLZ; atoms
bonded together) of air cause incoming meteors

*Clouds are mainly found in the lower part of the
atmosphere. Above them, the sky is clear.*

to burn or break up, so they usually fall
harmlessly to Earth's surface. Most important,
ozone in the stratosphere (STRA-tuh-SFIR; the
part of Earth's atmosphere between about 7 miles
[11 km] and 31 miles [50 km] above Earth)
absorbs potentially harmful ultraviolet (having a
wavelength shorter than those of visible light and
longer than those of X rays) light from the Sun.

Some of the other planets in the Solar System
have atmospheres that are too thin to provide
such protection. The rest have thick atmospheres
filled with poisonous gases, so high temperatures

The spectacular white trail left by a high-flying jet is created when the water in the exhaust fumes freezes to form ice particles as they hit the cold air at 35,000 feet (10,675 m).

and pressures make it impossible for living organisms like those found on Earth. In the Solar System, only Earth is known to have the right temperature, pressure, and gases to support life.

Earth's atmosphere is a mixture of gases called air. Nitrogen makes up about 78 percent of air at sea level. Oxygen makes up around 0.03 percent. Water vapor varies from low levels to up to 5 to 6 percent. There are also inert gases, which do not play a part in normal chemical reactions. These include 0.93 percent argon, with traces of neon, helium, krypton, and xenon. Traces of free hydrogen and ozone are also found at sea level.

Although none of them is present in large quantities, water vapor, carbon dioxide, and ozone are the most important gases in affecting Earth's weather and climate.

Atmospheric layers

The weight of air pressing from the top of the atmosphere to the layers below is called the atmospheric pressure. At sea level, it averages 14 pounds 11 ounces per square inch, or psi (1.03 kg/sq cm). Higher up, as the altitude increases, the atmospheric pressure decreases. The chemical composition of the atmosphere also changes.

Scientists have divided Earth's atmosphere into four distinct layers. The lowest is the

Thermosphere
(up to about 250 miles)

Mesopause

−130°F

Mesosphere

Stratopause

30°F

Stratosphere

Ozone maximum
(at about 15 miles)

Tropopause

−70°F   Troposphere

Average temperature

Height in miles

50

30

10

0

Earth's atmosphere has four main layers. These are the troposphere, stratosphere, mesosphere, and thermosphere.

The Ozone Layer

The ozone in the stratosphere protects Earth's surface and its living organisms from the harmful effects of ultraviolet (UV) radiation from the Sun. Short-wave UV radiation splits a two-atom molecule of oxygen (O_2) into two single atoms. The single atoms then combine with an oxygen molecule to make ozone (O_3). This reaction absorbs the UV energy. However, other UV wavelengths can split the ozone molecule once again into a two-atom oxygen molecule and a free oxygen atom.

There is a delicate balance between these two reactions in the atmosphere, about 30 miles (50 km) above Earth's surface. Here, the temperature can reach as high as 30°F (–1°C) as the Sun's energy is absorbed. Even small decreases in the ozone layer of the stratosphere will result in more UV radiation reaching the surface. More UV radiation will result in an increase in skin cancer in all animals. This is a matter of great concern, particularly in countries such as Australia.

By the mid-1970s, scientists had made an important discovery. Chlorofluorocarbons (CFCs) are used in aerosol sprays and as liquids in refrigerators and air-conditioning systems. When chlorofluorocarbons escape into the atmosphere, they can reduce the amount of ozone in the stratosphere. Holes have already been discovered in the ozone layer, particularly near the poles, where harmful UV radiation can reach Earth. International cooperation is currently under way to reduce, and hopefully eliminate, the use of CFCs before the ozone in the stratosphere is destroyed.

troposphere, which extends to some 5 to 10 miles (8 to 16 km) above the surface. It contains more than 75 percent of the total atmosphere by weight.

The troposphere gets its name from the Greek word *tropos*, which means "turning," because it is constantly mixing. Warm air rises and cool air sinks, causing the world's weather.

The average temperature at Earth's surface is 59°F (15°C). As the altitude increases, the temperature drops. At 10 miles (16 km) high, it can be as low as –70°F (–57°C). The tropopause is the boundary that exists between the troposphere and the next layer—called the stratosphere—and here the temperature stops falling.

The stratosphere extends from around 6 to 30 miles (10 to 50 km) above Earth's surface. Here, the ozone layer absorbs much of the energy from the Sun, and the temperature gradually rises, reaching as high as 30°F (–1°C). There is little or no water vapor there, so there are no weather systems. Airline pilots prefer to fly in the stratosphere because the air is clear. There are also strong and steady winds, called the jet stream, which they can use.

The stratosphere, and its ozone layer, absorbs harmful radiation. High-energy particles from space, called cosmic rays, collide with air molecules and break up. Ozone also reduces the harmful effects of the Sun's ultraviolet light.

The next highest layer is the mesosphere, which extends from 30 to 50 miles (48 to 81 km) above Earth's surface. There is very little ozone to absorb the Sun's radiation, so temperatures begin to fall again. They can drop as low as –171°F (–113°C). Meteors from space begin to burn up when they enter the mesosphere. As they fall, they generally burn up completely.

Above the mesosphere is the thermosphere, stretching from 50 to 250 miles (80 to 400 km) above Earth's surface. The radiation from the

Sun is absorbed by oxygen molecules in the thin air, and the temperature can rise to 3600°F (1980°C). Electrons get stripped from their atoms, forming electrically conductive regions. The area has another name, the ionosphere (eye-AH-nuh-sfir), because atoms missing some or all of their electrons are called ions. Conditions in the ionosphere can affect long-distance radio transmission and also produce the aurora borealis (northern lights) and the aurora australis (southern lights).

Only a tiny part of Earth's atmosphere—less than 0.01 percent—is contained in the thermosphere. The thermosphere's upper edge is called the exosphere. Here, the atmosphere is made up of hydrogen and helium, and it is so thin that there is almost no resistance to satellites and orbiting spacecraft. Some gas molecules can overcome Earth's gravity and escape into space. In this way, Earth is very slowly losing its atmosphere, but this will take billions of years.

History of the atmosphere

Earth's atmosphere today is different from how it was three billion years ago. Scientists have different theories about how it has evolved. There is little doubt that at one time there was no oxygen, so life as it is known today was impossible. Geologists (scientists who study the structure and history of rocks) have studied layers formed around two million years ago called banded ironstones. Before this time, iron was dissolved in the oceans and did not rust. When bacteria began to produce oxygen for the first time, iron in the sea oxidized and red banded ironstones were formed.

CHECK THESE OUT!
✔AIR PRESSURE
✔CARBON DIOXIDE
✔GLOBAL WARMING
✔METEOROLOGY
✔NITROGEN ✔OXYGEN
✔OZONE LAYER
✔STRATOSPHERE
✔WEATHER ✔WIND

LOOK CLOSER

CFCs and the Ozone Layer

Carbon is more important to life on Earth than oxygen. The complex part that carbon plays in life is called the carbon cycle.

Carbon dioxide in the atmosphere is dissolved in water droplets, which fall to Earth as rain. Most of it reaches the oceans. At the same time, carbon dioxide is released from decaying organisms and the respiration of living organisms. The amount that escapes from the oceans equals the amount that arrives in rain, and so the balance is maintained.

On land, carbon dioxide is taken from the air by plants in photosynthesis (FOH-toh-SIN-thuh-suhs; the way plants use light energy to make sugar). Animals eat the plants, and are eaten in turn by other animals. When the animals die, they are decomposed (broken down) by microorganisms, which return the carbon dioxide to the atmosphere. If organic matter does not decay, it is fossilized (preserved) as coal, oil, or peat. This can remain as a carbon store for millions of years.

Fossil fuels are burned today at an increasing rate, returning more carbon dioxide to the atmosphere than reaches Earth. Samples taken from ancient ice fields show that levels of carbon dioxide in the atmosphere are associated with worldwide temperature changes. The ice ages had the lowest levels, while warm tropical periods had high levels.

The concentration of carbon dioxide in the atmosphere is called the greenhouse effect. Scientists are concerned that the burning of fossil fuels will affect the lower atmosphere. Some have predicted that surface temperatures on Earth will rise as much as 9°F (5°C) over the next century, upsetting life on Earth as it is now.

Power stations burn coal to heat water. Burning coal increases carbon dioxide levels in the atmosphere.

Atom

Atoms are the basic building blocks that make up every possible thing in the Universe. The first person to suggest that matter consisted of atoms was Greek philosopher and scientist Democritus (around 460–around 370 B.C.E.). He proposed that any substance could be divided into small, indivisible units (the word atom comes from the Greek word for indivisible, *atomos*). He believed that the shape of these units gave the material its properties. In his thinking, liquids were composed of smooth, round atoms that could slip past each other with ease; solids were made of jagged, rough atoms that locked together to form a hard mass. Few people believed Democritus's theory—it seemed obvious that even the smallest visible grain of a substance could be smashed if it was hit hard enough.

Aristotle's theory of the elements

A few decades later, Greek philosopher Aristotle (384–322 B.C.E.) developed a different system for explaining matter. His idea was that there were

Although it was many years before his work was accepted by other scientists, it was John Dalton who realized that indivisible atoms of different weights reacted in fixed proportions.

HIGHLIGHTS

♦ Greek philosopher Democritus first proposed the concept of the atom almost 2,500 years ago.

♦ In the late 19th century, atoms were thought to be masses of positive charge with negatively charged electrons spread throughout them like the fruit in a plum pudding.

♦ Atoms are now known to consist of protons and neutrons bundled into tiny central nuclei and surrounded by clouds of electrons. Every atom has an equal number of protons and electrons

four basic elements—air, earth, fire, and water—and that mixing these elements in the correct way could make any substance. According to this theory, bricks were made by adding fire to earth in a kiln. Aristotle's theory became more widely believed than Democritus's theory—it made more sense in terms of everyday experience. Aristotle did not believe that these elements were made of particles: in his view, all matter was divisible—it could be broken down into smaller and smaller pieces without limit.

Early modern theories

The theory of the four elements remained popular until the 17th century, when scientists were starting to identify more elements than the four of Aristotle's theory. A radical change in thinking was brought about by experiments done by French scientist Joseph-Louis Proust (1778–1850). He discovered that chemical substances always react together in exactly the same proportions by weight. For example, one gram of hydrogen reacts with eight grams of oxygen to form nine grams of water; one ounce of hydrogen reacts with eight ounces of oxygen to produce nine ounces of water, and so on.

It was British scientist John Dalton (1766–1844) who realized that Proust's law of constant composition was inconsistent with Aristotle's view of matter: if the elements did not consist of particles, why did they always react in exactly the same ratios? Dalton proposed that Democritus's model—with elements composed of atoms—was correct. He pointed out that the constant weight ratios that Proust had observed could be explained by atoms of different weights reacting in fixed ratios (1:1, 3:2, and so on).

Atomic mass

By 1803, Dalton had calculated the weights of the atoms of a number of elements relative to the weight of a hydrogen atom. The term *atomic mass* arose from these calculations. The atomic mass of an element is defined as the mass of a number of atoms of that element divided by the mass of the same number of hydrogen atoms. Carbon had an atomic mass of approximately 12 on Dalton's scale. The modern definition is slightly different in that the most common form (isotope) of carbon is taken to have an atomic mass of exactly 12; all other atomic masses are defined relative to that value.

The structure of the atom

Despite the growing knowledge of the chemical behavior of the elements, nobody knew what atoms consisted of. A breakthrough came in 1897 when British physicist J. J. Thomson (1856–1940) discovered the electron while he was studying cathode rays (beams of negatively charged particles that are produced by metals when they are heated and connected to a negative voltage). By studying the behavior of these beams, Thomson calculated the mass of the electron to be about one–two thousandth of the mass of a hydrogen atom—the lightest atom—with an atomic mass of one unit. Thomson reasoned that, in addition to electrons, atoms must contain positive charges in order to balance the negative charges of the electrons. He envisaged the atom as a mass of positive charge, with electrons scattered through it—this was called the plum pudding model. In the periodic table, each successive element would have one electron more than the previous element, and another dose of positive charge to balance the electron. He gave the name atomic number to

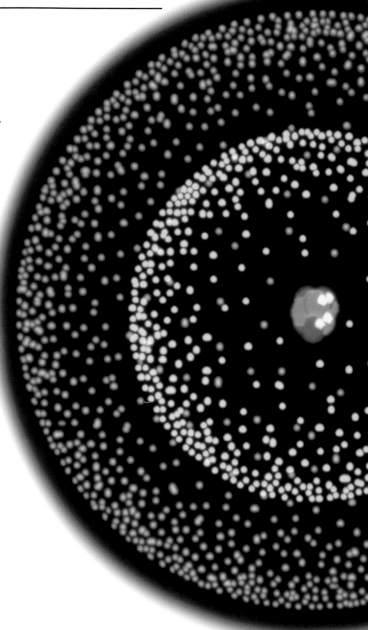

An atom consists of a central, positive nucleus with clouds of negative electrons in layers around it. The dots in this illustration show where the few electrons might be at any given moment.

the count of electrons (and positive charges) in an atom of a given element. The atomic number is always a whole number and is used to place the elements in order in the periodic table, starting with hydrogen (atomic number 1) in the top left-hand corner of the table.

There was no real evidence to defend the plum pudding model of the atom, and the curious fact remained that the atomic masses of the elements did not increase steadily with the atomic number, which would be the case if atoms consisted only of positive charges and electrons. For example, helium (atomic number 2) has an atomic mass four times that of hydrogen (atomic number 1), rather than two times. British physicist Ernest Rutherford (1871–1937) set out to discover the real structure of atoms by firing alpha particles at an extremely thin gold foil. Alpha particles are fast-moving particles that are produced by some radioactive elements; they have a positive charge twice the size of an electron's negative charge. If the plum pudding model were true, alpha particles would have no difficulty in passing through a thin gold foil. Rutherford's experiment showed that while most of the alpha particles did indeed pass through the film, they were often knocked off course, and some even bounced back. Rutherford observed, "It was almost as incredible as if you had fired a 15-inch shell at a piece of tissue paper and it came back and hit you."

Rutherford concluded that the positive charge of the gold atoms had to be concentrated into a small space at the center of the atom—the nucleus—to account for those alpha particles that bounced back. This concentration of positive charge would then be enough to repel those positive alpha particles that hit a nucleus squarely, since like charges repel each other. Rutherford also proposed the existence of a heavy, positively charged particle—the proton—that was the nucleus of the hydrogen atom, and an equally heavy but uncharged particle—the neutron—that would make up the atomic mass of

LOOK CLOSER

Periodic Table

By the mid-19th century, most scientists agreed with Dalton's view that the elements were composed of atoms, and that the atoms of each element had a characteristic weight. More elements were being discovered and the chemical properties of the elements were being studied and documented.

A curious feature started to be noticed in the chemical behavior of the elements: if the elements were listed in order of increasing atomic mass, roughly the same chemical properties would be shared by every eighth element. For example, lithium (the third element) and sodium (the eleventh element) react with the same types of elements under similar conditions to give similar products. The repetition of characteristics over a period of eight (or in some cases 18) elements is called periodicity. It was Russian scientist Dmitry Mendeleyev (1834–1907) who first organized the elements into a periodic table, in which atomic weight increases from left to right across a period (row) and from top to bottom, and elements with similar properties are all in the same column. The periodic table helped chemists to organize their results and prompted them to look for the elements missing from the table.

heavier atoms: a hydrogen atom consists of one proton and one electron; a helium atom consists of two protons, two neutrons, and two electrons; and a lithium atom consists of three protons, four neutrons, and three electrons.

The nuclei of atoms are tiny bundles of protons and neutrons in roughly equal numbers, surrounded by a cloud of electrons that occupies nearly all the space of the atom but accounts for a fraction of a thousandth of its weight. The electrons move around in layers called shells, and only the electrons in the outermost shell are involved in chemical reactions.

CHECK THESE OUT!
✔CATHODE RAY ✔ELECTRON ✔ELEMENT ✔ION
✔ISOTOPE ✔MOLECULE ✔NUCLEAR PHYSICS
✔PARTICLE PHYSICS ✔PERIODIC TABLE ✔PROTON
✔RADIOACTIVITY ✔SUBATOMIC STRUCTURE

Aurora

Spectacular, flickering displays of light seen in the night sky in the polar regions are called auroras (uh-ROHR-uhz). The lights most often appear as shifting, shimmering curtains of different colors, but curls, arcs, and rays are also seen. These beautiful, natural light shows are named after Aurora, the Roman goddess of the dawn. When seen in the Northern Hemisphere, they are called the northern lights or the aurora borealis. In the Southern Hemisphere, they are called the southern lights or the aurora australis.

Although not frequently seen, auroras are best observed within oval-shaped zones close to the north and south magnetic poles. These areas are called auroral zones. In the far north, the displays are most often seen across northern Canada, Alaska, and in northern Europe. In the far south, they are best observed from Antarctica in the winter months.

Close to the auroral zone, viewers see auroras almost overhead. From a distance of more than 600 miles (100 km), the curtains appear to touch the horizon. When viewed from space via satellites, auroras appear as oval rings of light over the poles.

What causes auroras?

Scientists puzzled for centuries over what caused auroras. Some believed they were the result of sunlight reflecting off the ice sheets in the polar regions. Others believed they were caused by light refracting (bending) as it passed through ice crystals in the upper atmosphere, producing an effect similar to a rainbow. Neither of these explanations is correct.

These shimmering lights are related to Earth being a giant magnet. Its magnetic field forms a loop that connects the North and South Poles like the field of a huge bar magnet. Auroras are produced when high-energy particles given off by the Sun hit Earth's atmosphere near the North and South Poles. The particles strike the

This photograph of aurora borealis—the northern lights—was taken in Anchorage, Alaska.

HIGHLIGHTS

♦ Auroras are natural displays of colored light most often seen near the North and South Poles.

♦ Auroras are caused by high-energy particles striking gas molecules in the atmosphere high above the poles.

♦ Most auroras are green in color. This color is produced by solar particles hitting oxygen atoms in the upper atmosphere. A red tinge results when solar particles strike the nitrogen atoms present at lower levels, or strike the oxygen, hydrogen, and helium atoms present at very high levels.

atmosphere near the poles because they are drawn toward Earth along magnetic lines of force. High in the atmosphere, they react with atoms of gases such as oxygen and nitrogen, causing the atoms to give off light. When the

atoms of gas are bombarded by solar particles, they absorb a certain amount of energy and become excited, which means that an electron around the atom's nucleus has been moved from its normal state of energy to a higher energy level. As the electron returns to its normal state, the energy is released in the form of light.

Auroras are constantly moving and changing, because the streams of solar particles reaching Earth—called a solar wind—vary in strength. Sometimes the emissions are more powerful, arriving in powerful bursts.

Colored lights

Most auroras happen in the atmosphere within a band 60 to 190 miles (100 to 305 km) above Earth's surface. The upper edge of the curtain of light is generally less distinct than the lower edge. Auroras appear in different colors and are classed as A through F, according to their color. Type C auroras—the most common type—are completely green. Type A auroras are green curtains tinged with red at the top. Type B are green with a red lower border. Type E are similar to B but are fast-moving. Type D auroras are red and much less common. Type F auroras occur at high altitudes and have a blue-purple color.

LOOK CLOSER

Artificial Auroras

Auroras are produced naturally by solar particles bombarding gases in the atmosphere. They can also be produced artificially, by electrons given off during high-altitude atom bomb tests. In 1958, an explosion above Johnston Atoll in the Pacific Ocean produced an impressive aurora 2,000 miles (3,200 km) to the south, near the island of Samoa.

They are seen at twilight, and their color is affected by the rays of the setting sun.

The different colors seen in auroras are mainly due to the fact that different gases predominate in Earth's atmosphere at different heights. Each gas gives off visible light of a different color as its atoms return to their normal state after being excited. At heights of over 60 miles (100 km) above the surface, oxygen atoms predominate. They give off mainly green light after being excited. Lower levels of the atmosphere contain nitrogen as well as oxygen atoms. When solar particles have enough energy to penetrate the atmosphere to this level, the nitrogen atoms give off red light, causing a type D aurora. Very high in the atmosphere, hydrogen, helium, and oxygen atoms also give off mainly red light as they return to their normal state.

The most common auroras are curtains of light with a sharp boundary at the bottom and a less clearly defined upper edge. They are called discrete auroras. Pulsating auroras are a second type of aurora, which flicker, as their name suggests. Within minutes, an aurora can change appearance dramatically. Discrete auroras change continually, developing rays, arcs, bands, and sometimes even curls and spirals. Pulsating auroras follow discrete auroras and are less bright. They look like patches of dim light turning on and off and sometimes last for hours.

CHECK THESE OUT!

✔ASTRONOMY ✔ATMOSPHERE
✔EARTH ✔ELECTRON ✔SPECTROSCOPY ✔SUN

Australasia

The geographic region covering Australia and New Guinea

At one time, the name Australasia (AWS-truh-LAY-zhuh) applied to all the land in the southwest Pacific: Australia and Tasmania, New Zealand, New Guinea (GIN-ee), the Solomon Islands, New Caledonia, and many other smaller islands. Nowadays, however, most geographers call this large area Oceania (OH-shee-AN-ee-uh). Australasia is the part of Oceania that includes the continent of Australia and the island of New Guinea. Politically, New Guinea is divided into two. The western half of the island, Irian Barat, is owned by Indonesia. The eastern half and its offshore islands make up the independent state of Papua New Guinea, which is under the protection of the Australian government.

Geology and evolution

Earth's crust is made up of a number of plates called tectonic plates. Australasia lies on the Australian–Indian plate. This plate runs along the southern edge of Indonesia and the northern edge of New Guinea, through the Solomon Islands, Vanatu, and Fiji to Samoa, then south through Tonga and the Kermadec Islands to New Zealand.

HIGHLIGHTS

◆ New Guinea lies on the edge of the Australian–Indian tectonic plate. Australia lies in the middle of this plate.

◆ Geographically isolated for 50 million years, Australia has evolved many unique species of living organisms.

Movement on the northern edge of the plate has resulted in volcanic mountains, such as Puncak Jaya in New Guinea. Although it is only a few degrees south of the equator (ih-KWAY-tuhr; an imaginary circle around Earth at equal distances from the North and South Poles), its peak is permanently snowcapped. Australia, however, lies in the middle of the eastern part of the plate. There has been no mountain-building there in the past 60 million years.

The western part of Australia consists of a large area of ancient rocks called the Western Australian Shield. In places, it is covered by a thin layer of more recent sedimentary rocks. In the eastern quarter of the continent, the Great Dividing Range of low mountains is between 570 and 225 million years old.

A number of the islands of Papua New Guinea are volcanic. Mount Tavurvur, below, is an active volcano.

Australia was once part of the great southern supercontinent Gondwana (gon-DWAH-nuh). Gondwana began to break apart 135 million years ago, and Australia was gradually carried northward to its present position. The continent has been separated from other continents and the Indonesian islands for the past 50 million years. This has allowed the evolution of species of living organisms found nowhere else on Earth.

Among the unique animal life found in Australia are the marsupials (mahr-SOO-pee-uhlz) and the monotremes. Marsupials are mammals that bear their young in a pouch on the mother's belly, like kangaroos. Monotremes are egg-laying mammals. There are two types, the duck-billed platypus and the echidna (ee-KID-nuh). New Guinea also has many unique species of orchids, birds of paradise, and flightless birds called cassowaries (KAS-uh-WEHR-eez).

Physical geography

Because there has been no mountain-building in Australia for 60 million years, most of the continent is very low and flat. Only 6 percent of its 3 million square miles (7.8 million sq km) is over 2,000 feet (610 m) above sea level. The highest point is the 7,310-foot (2,228-m) Mount Kosciusko, in the Snowy Mountains of southeastern New South Wales.

Most Australian rivers flow only now and then. The exception is the Murray River, which rises in the snowfields of Mount Kosciusko and

A map of Australia and New Guinea and some of the continent's surrounding islands.

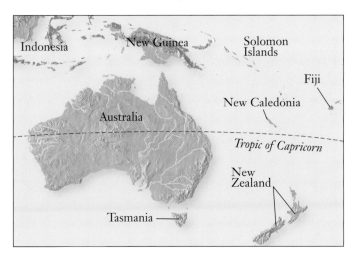

Indonesia · New Guinea · Solomon Islands · Fiji · New Caledonia · Australia · *Tropic of Capricorn* · New Zealand · Tasmania

LOOK CLOSER

Minerals

The rocks of Australia, particularly in the west, are rich in important minerals (substances mined from the ground). These include gold, silver, diamonds, opals (multicolored gems), the aluminum ore bauxite, iron ore, coal, oil and natural gas, and uranium.

The deposits of iron ore in the Hamersley Range and Robe River regions of Western Australia are among the largest in the world. The reserves total several billion tons. Large reserves of oil and natural gas have been found beneath the Bass Strait, between the mainland and Tasmania.

Gold was first discovered in New South Wales in 1851. The biggest gold rush occurred at Kalgoorlie in Western Australia in the 1890s. Opal has been mined in South Australia since 1911.

flows westward for 1,600 miles (2,570 km) to reach the sea near Adelaide. Even the Murray has been known to dry up sometimes, and there are no big permanent lakes. However, the desert basins of central and western Australia do sometimes contain numerous large salt lakes such as Lake Eyre (ehr).

Climate

Most of Australia lies in tropical latitudes (distances from the equator) between 15 and 35 degrees south. It is therefore mostly hot and dry. Because the continent is so large, humidity from the sea cannot reach the interior, and there are few mountains to produce rainclouds. Over two-thirds of Australia receives less than 20 inches (510 mm) of rain a year, and one-third receives less than 10 inches (250 mm), similar to the Arizona deserts. In these parts, daytime summer temperatures are regularly higher than 100°F (38°C). The wettest parts of the continent are the east coast and the island of Tasmania. New Guinea lies between 1 and 10 degrees south. Its rain forests have an equatorial climate—hot, wet, and humid all year round.

CHECK THESE OUT!
✔CONTINENT ✔ISLAND ✔OCEANIA

Avalanche

A large mass of snow, ice, or rock debris moving rapidly down a mountain slope

One of the most spectacular and destructive types of all natural forces is an avalanche. Avalanches pose a serious danger to people living or traveling in mountain regions. Their destructive power is incredible. Thousands of tons of snow race downhill at speeds of over 100 miles per hour (160 km/h), uprooting trees and wrecking buildings on the way. The shock wave (blast of air) that accompanies an avalanche can shatter windows and tear doors off their hinges. The worst avalanche in the history of the United States occurred in 1910. It swept two trains off their tracks and killed 96 people.

Snow avalanches

Snow avalanches can happen wherever there are mountains with open slopes and heavy snow. They are caused when the weight of snow on a mountain slope overcomes the forces that hold the snow in place. An avalanche can be set off by a fresh snowfall, a sudden rise in temperature, or a wide variety of other events, from earthquakes to passing skiers. Snow avalanches can pick up earth, rocks, and even trees as they sweep downhill. They are classed as either loose-snow avalanches or slab avalanches. A loose-snow avalanche begins as a small slide and then gathers more and more snow as it moves downhill. In a slab avalanche, a large area of snow that has been packed into a slab falls away all at once.

A large snow avalanche on Mount McKinley in Alaska. Snow avalanches are common on mountains with open slopes and heavy snowfall.

Both kinds of avalanches happen whether the snow is wet or dry. Wet-snow avalanches usually happen in spring when temperatures begin to rise. The heavy, waterlogged snow can do great damage, and it sets like concrete when it stops moving. Dry-snow avalanches can move very fast, often pushing a shock wave ahead of them.

HIGHLIGHTS

♦ Avalanches threaten animals, plants, people, and settlements in mountain regions.

♦ Avalanches can be controlled by preventing the buildup of snow on steep slopes or by deflecting the flow of avalanches that have already started.

Avalanches take place only on slopes of a certain angle, where enough snow has built up and then become unstable. Most take place on slopes with angles between 30 and 45 degrees. The amount of snow needed for an avalanche to happen varies according to conditions. Avalanches have been known in as little as 6 inches (15 cm) of snow, and where snow lies as deep as 15 feet (4.5 m) or more. Snow can become unstable due to weak layers within or under the snow, which can provide a sliding surface for a slab of snow, or due to a rise in temperature, which loosens the bonds between snow grains and results in a loose-snow avalanche.

The event that sets off an avalanche is known as the trigger. Natural triggers include further heavy snowfalls, rain, drifting snow, or a sudden rise in temperature. Avalanches can also be triggered naturally by earthquakes, smaller earth tremors, or by falling ice. Artificial triggers include explosives, sonic booms, and people.

Ice avalanches

Ice avalanches happen when large blocks of ice fall from a glacier. They may be triggered by earth tremors or glacier movement itself. In 1970 at Mount Huascaran in the Andes Mountains in Peru, an earthquake dislodged the mountain's ice cap. The falling ice triggered unstable slopes of rock and mud lower down the mountain, creating a giant avalanche. The avalanche raced down the valley and engulfed everything in its path. Around 70,000 people died in the disaster.

LOOK CLOSER

Controlling Avalanches

Snow avalanches pose a serious danger to humans, settlements, animals, and vegetation in snowy mountain ranges. In the United States, avalanches are monitored and controlled by scientists and trained ski patrols.

Avalanches can be controlled in two ways. The buildup of deep, dangerous snow can be prevented. Alternatively, the flow of those avalanches that have already begun can be prevented or stopped. Prevention measures include building fences along the windward sides of mountain ridges, which cause wind-blown snow to be deposited there instead of building up on downwind slopes.

The European Alps hold some of the world's oldest avalanche deflection features. Some 19th-century churches there have been built with a V-shaped gable facing uphill, which splits the snow like a ship's prow. Local laws in the Alps forbid trees to be cut down above villages, as dense forests can help to protect settlements by blocking the path of avalanches higher up.

More modern human-made deflection structures include fences, ramps, and snow sheds that divert the flow of an avalanche or carry it over the top of features such as roads and railroads.

Debris avalanches

A debris (duh-BREE) avalanche consists of a mass of rock fragments that are mixed with mud and water or air. The debris (broken pieces) behaves like a liquid as it sweeps downhill at speeds of up to 200 miles per hour (320 km/h). The destruction brought by debris avalanches is similar to that caused by landslides, rockfalls, and mudflows. As with snow avalanches, debris avalanches happen when an unstable mass of rock fragments is set in motion by a trigger. Events that may trigger debris avalanches include heavy rainfall, earthquakes or earth tremors, and volcanic eruptions.

CHECK THESE OUT!
✔ EROSION ✔ LANDFORM ✔ MOUNTAIN

Battery

A portable source of energy that produces electricity through chemical reactions

Portable power supplies that produce a limited amount of electrical energy through a chemical reaction are called batteries. Available in all shapes and sizes, batteries suit a range of electrical appliances. They are often used in places where normal electrical supplies cannot be fitted. A pacemaker implanted in a person's chest keeps his or her heart beating regularly thanks to a long-life battery inside it. Satellites in space often use batteries to store the energy generated by their solar panels (large, thin panels that generate electricity from sunlight) to keep them working when they move into Earth's shadow.

How batteries work

A battery is a collection of electrochemical cells connected in series. A low-voltage battery may include only one cell. Although there are many different types of cells and batteries, they all have the same basic components (parts). Inside each cell there is a positive electrode (electrical terminal or connection) and a negative electrode, plus a liquid that conducts electricity (called an electrolyte) in between them. When an electric circuit is connected to the outside of the battery (for example, when a flashlight with a battery in it is switched on), a chemical reaction occurs in between the electrolyte and the electrodes. Ions (atoms that have gained or lost electrons) move from one electrode to the other through the

HIGHLIGHTS

♦ Batteries make electricity using chemical reactions that produce ions and electrons. The movement of these charged particles makes an electrical current flow through a circuit.

♦ There are many different types of batteries, including zinc–carbon, long-life alkaline, nickel–cadmium, and lead–acid.

♦ Primary batteries cannot be recharged. Secondary batteries (accumulators) are rechargeable.

electrolyte. Meanwhile, electrons move from one electrode to the other through the outside circuit. The movement of electrons and ions together makes a current flow.

This is a general description of what happens inside a battery. The reactions that take place in a battery depend on the chemicals from which the electrodes and the electrolyte are made.

Flashlights typically use zinc–carbon batteries. These have a negative electrode made of zinc, a positive electrode that consists of a carbon rod surrounded by manganese dioxide (MnO_2), and an electrolyte that is a jelly of zinc chloride ($ZnCl_2$) and ammonium chloride (NH_4Cl).

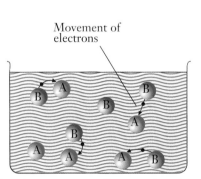

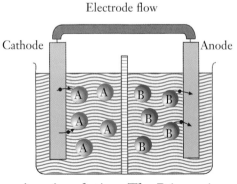

An electron transfer reaction between ions in solution. The B ions give up electrons to the A ions. By separating the kinds of ions with a porous barrier and adding electrodes, electrons are forced to travel through the wire by the same reaction.

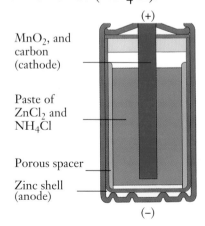

A cross section of a zinc–carbon dry cell.

Types of batteries

Zinc–carbon batteries are also called dry cells because, unlike some other batteries, they do not use a liquid electrolyte. One drawback of zinc–carbon batteries is their short life. Long-life batteries use an alkali such as potassium hydroxide as the electrolyte. This is why they are also called alkaline batteries. Hearing aids, quartz (KWARTS) watches, and calculators use a type of long-lasting battery called a button cell. This has a negative electrode made from powdered zinc, a positive electrode made from mercury oxide and graphite, and a potassium hydroxide (alkaline) electrolyte just like a long-life battery.

All these batteries are called primary batteries. They cannot easily be recharged and have to be thrown away when they run out of power. Another type of battery is called a secondary battery, rechargeable battery, or accumulator. The lead–acid batteries used in automobile engines are one example of this. The nickel–cadmium rechargeable batteries used in cassette players are another. Unlike a primary battery, a secondary battery can be recharged simply by passing an electric current through it in the opposite direction to which the battery would normally generate a current by itself. Other rechargeable batteries include nickel–metal–hydride and lithium ion. Nickel cadmium batteries should be completely discharged before they are recharged. Other rechargeable batteries can be brought up to full charge at any time; this has made them a popular choice for laptop computers and cellular phones.

Historical development

The first battery was invented in 1800 by Italian physicist Alessandro Volta (1745–1827) who conducted pioneering (new and exploratory) experiments into electricity during the 18th century. Quite unlike modern batteries, Volta's voltaic pile was built up from many separate layers, each one a cell consisting of a disk of silver (the positive electrode), a disk of cardboard or leather soaked in salt water (the electrolyte), and a disk of zinc (the negative electrode).

Volta's battery had been constructed largely through trial and error, but the chemical theory of how it operated was eventually worked out by

EVERYDAY SCIENCE

Batteries for Electric Cars

Automobile engines contribute to smog (smoke and fog) and use fuels, such as gasoline, that are running out. Engineers hope to produce cleaner and more environmentally friendly cars by using electric battery-powered motors. Normal batteries are not powerful enough, and experimental electric vehicles can only travel about 90 to 110 miles (150 to 180 km) before their batteries have to be recharged (like in the picture below).

Engineers are developing better ways of storing energy. The cars of the future may be powered by fuel cells, which produce electricity from a continuous supply of hydrogen gas piped in from outside. They are twice as efficient as internal combustion engines and produce water as a waste product.

English chemist Sir Humphry Davy (1778–1829). Improved designs were also produced by English chemist John Frederic Daniell (1790–1845) and Sir William Grove (1811–1896). They used acid liquids as the electrolyte, which was both inconvenient and potentially dangerous. This problem was solved by French chemist Georges Leclanché (1839–1882), who invented the dry cell used in most of today's disposable batteries.

Rechargeable batteries were developed in the 19th century. German chemist Christian Schönbein (1799–1868) was the first to discover that a battery might be regenerated by passing a current through it in the reverse direction.

CHECK THESE OUT!
✔ELECTRICITY ✔ENERGY

Binary Star

A pair of stars held in orbit around each other by the force of gravity

Only a few stars in the galaxy travel through space on their own like the Sun. Usually two or more stars are found orbiting around each other. Systems with two stars in them are called binary (BY-nuh-ree) stars. Astronomers (scientists who study planets and stars) sometimes also use the name for systems with three stars or more. By studying binaries, astronomers can find out important information about both stars in a system. Sometimes, when the stars get close enough together, they can interact to produce unusual effects.

What is a binary star?

Astronomers think that nearly all binary star systems formed together from the same original nebula (NEH-byuh-luh; gas cloud). A few binaries might be stars whose gravity captured each other during a close encounter, but the chances of this happening are so slim that they cannot account for the huge number of binaries (90 percent of stars) present in the galaxy.

Some stars appear close to each other in the sky because they are in the same direction from Earth, but one might be hundreds of light-years away from the other. These line-of-sight effects are called optical doubles and are not related.

This photograph shows the cool red giant star Mira A (left) and its hot companion.

Types of binaries

There are several different types of binaries. Astronomers name them according to the way they are discovered. The most obvious are visual binaries—systems where both stars can be seen separately with the naked eye or with a telescope. The best-known double stars in the sky are visual binaries, such as the Alpha Centauri system and the Sirius system (the brightest star in the sky and its dim companion).

Sometimes, bright stars have faint companions that are lost in their glare. Until the 1930s, this was the case with Sirius, but astronomers still knew it was a binary system because of a slight wobble in Sirius's movement through space. This type of binary, which can be detected by careful astrometry (A-STRAH-meh-tree; measurement of the star's movement), is called an astrometric (AS-troh-MEH-trik) binary.

Most binary stars are too far away and move too slowly to be separated astrometrically or visually, yet astronomers can identify them by analyzing their light. When the light from a star is passed through a prism (PRIH-zum; a transparent body that separates the different colors in light), it splits into a rainbow spectrum, with dark lines across it caused by elements in the star's atmosphere. By creating spectra on Earth, astronomers know where these dark lines should form but find that the lines from stars are out of place. This is because the star is moving relative to Earth. If it is moving toward Earth, its light is shifted to the blue end of the spectrum. If it is moving away, it is shifted to the red end.

Astronomers often find that even after a star's movement has been allowed for, the spectral lines are slowly shifting position toward the red, then the blue, and back again. This is because the bright star is moving backward and forward as it orbits with its companion—a system called a spectroscopic binary.

A final type of binary happens when the stars pass in front of each other as seen from Earth. If this happens, then the combined brightness of the stars drops as one star is hidden behind the other. This is called an eclipsing binary.

Information from binaries

Because binary stars are locked in orbit, and obey the laws of these orbits, astronomers can find out much about them. If the system is an optical double, the distance between the stars can be worked out and the period (duration) of their orbit around each other can be observed. This can be used to work out the combined mass of the two stars in the system. The mass of each star then depends on how close it is to the system's common center of gravity. Using the masses of stars in binary systems, British astronomer Arthur Eddington (1882–1944) worked out the relationship between a star's mass and its brightness. Tricks like this can also be used to work out the properties of stars in spectroscopic and eclipsing binaries.

Binaries reveal unusual types of star systems. Sometimes, the two stars that formed together to make the binary have very different masses. The larger one rushes through its life cycle at high

DISCOVERERS

Discovery of Binaries

German-born British astronomer William Herschel (1738–1822), assisted by his sister Caroline Herschel (1750–1848), was the first person to use the term *binary star*. Astronomers already suspected that there might be star systems that orbited each other. Herschel compiled a star catalog, containing many double stars. At first he thought these were all line-of-sight effects. When he realized this was unlikely, he measured the movements of the star Castor, in the constellation Gemini, and its companion. In 1804, he published the evidence that showed these stars were orbiting each other, but even he could have had no idea of quite how many stars would eventually turn out to be binaries.

speed. For stars like the Sun, this ends in a white dwarf stage, with most of the star's mass concentrated in a volume the size of Earth. For bigger stars, the result is an even denser neutron star the size of a city, or a black hole, where all the mass seems concentrated in one point. If the stars are close enough together, the companion's gravity can pull material off the visible star. With white dwarfs, this can create a nova. When this happens, gas from the visible star forms an atmosphere around the companion and explodes, making the system blaze much brighter for several days. If the companion is a neutron star or a black hole, the results are even more violent.

CHECK THESE OUT!
✔ASTRONOMY ✔BLACK HOLE
✔CONSTELLATION ✔DOPPLER EFFECT
✔ECLIPSE ✔GRAVITY ✔PULSAR ✔STAR ✔UNIVERSE

Biochemistry

The study of the compounds and chemical processes associated with living things

During the 1800s, scientists made a number of discoveries that showed that the processes of life could be described as chemical reactions. These discoveries provided the basis for the field of science called biochemistry.

Proteins

Proteins are an essential part of living organisms. They make up more than half the mass of animals—not accounting for the mass of water— and form cell tissues, hormones, and enzymes. The building blocks of proteins are amino (uh-MEE-NOH) acids, which are simple organic (carbon- and hydrogen-containing) molecules containing an amine group ($-NH_2$) and a carboxylic acid group ($-CO_2H$). In proteins, amino acids join together when the amine group in one amino acid reacts with the carboxylic acid group in another. The reaction is called a condensation reaction because it produces water. The link between the amino acid is called a peptide bond.

At the start of the 20th century, scientists tried to discover how the amino acids linked together to form proteins. In the condensation reaction,

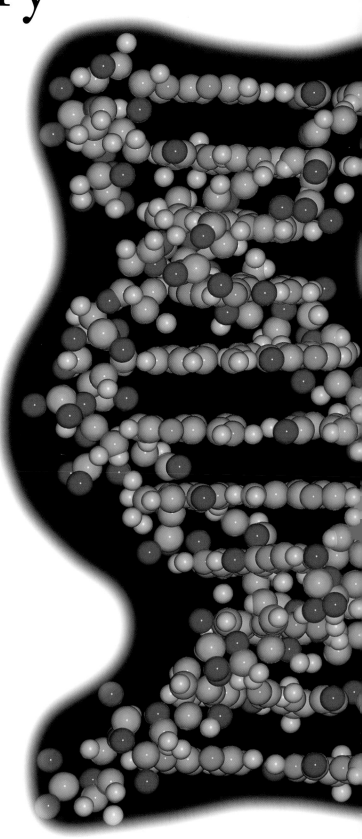

HIGHLIGHTS

♦ Proteins form cell tissues, hormones, and enzymes. They are essential for living organisms.

♦ Amino acids are the building blocks of proteins.

♦ Proteins called enzymes work as catalysts, helping reactions happen within the body.

♦ Francis Crick and James Watson shared the Nobel Prize for physiology or medicine in 1962 for explaining the structure of DNA.

This computer artwork of part of a strand of DNA shows atoms as spheres. The atoms are color-coded: carbon (blue), oxygen (red), hydrogen (yellow), nitrogen (green), and phosphorus (orange).

the amino acid that has given its amine group to the peptide bond still has a free carboxylic acid group. The other amino acid also has a free amino group. Either end of the molecule can react in the same way to form another linkage, so chains of amino acids grow, each one joined by peptide bonds to its two neighbors in the chain. A chain of amino acids is called a polypeptide. Some other chain molecules (polymers) join up with peptide bonds. Nylon is an example of this.

In the 1950s, scientists discovered how these building blocks could have formed early in Earth's development. The first step in finding the composition of proteins was to discover how many amino acids combined in a chain. Swedish chemist Theodor Svedberg (1884–1971) discovered a way to measure the weight of protein molecules using a machine called an ultracentrifuge that spins at 45,000 revolutions per minute (rpm). Tubes attached to the arms of such a centrifuge experience a force 5,000 times greater than the force due to gravity. The tubes swing outward as the centrifuge operates, and the heavier components of mixtures in the tubes settle out. Svedberg devised a way to calculate the weights of molecules from the position in the tube at which they settle out. Using this technique, he calculated the weight of a hemoglobin molecule to be 68,000 times that of a hydrogen atom. Since then, techniques such as chemical analysis, X-ray diffraction, and computer modeling have allowed scientists to calculate the sequences of amino acids in protein chains, and the ways in which the chains themselves take shape in three dimensions.

DISCOVERERS

The Founders of Biochemistry

At the start of the 19th century, chemistry and medicine were completely separate fields of study. Scientists believed molecules in living beings had some form of life force that could not be created in the laboratory from mineral substances. In 1828, German chemist Friedrich Wöhler (1800–1882) discovered that when he heated a solution of ammonium cyanate (NH_4CNO), the water boiled off and left a substance called urea (NH_2CONH_2). Both substances contain the same elements in the same proportions, but ammonium cyanate can be made from its elements by a series of simple chemical reactions. Urea, which is found in the urine of animals, would be impossible to make in the laboratory if the theory of life force were true. By performing this experiment, Wöhler produced the first piece of evidence that vitalism—the theory of life force—was untrue.

German chemist Justus von Liebig (1803–1873) studied fermentation reactions with Wöhler. Liebig went on to study the chemical composition of foods and bodily excretions, proposing that the energy for life came from the body burning fats and carbohydrates. Liebig also studied compositions of plants. He proposed that plants grew by taking in carbon dioxide and water from the air, and ammonia from soil. By studying the chemistry of animals and plants, Liebig was one of the first people to link botany, chemistry, and medicine.

In 1846, French physiologist Claude Bernard (1813–1878) discovered that the pancreases of animals secrete a fluid that aids the breakdown of fats. He later studied the function of the liver and the processes that occur in the living body in terms of chemical reactions. German chemist Emil Fischer (1852–1919) synthesized glucose and other sugars. He discovered the chemical structures of natural compounds including caffeine and certain sugars. He also discovered that proteins could be hydrolyzed (split up by water) into simple compounds called amino acids. By 1902, when Fischer received a Nobel Prize for chemistry for his work on sugars, the study of the chemistry of life had been named biochemistry for the first time.

EVERYDAY SCIENCE

Bioremediation—Hungry Bugs

For gardeners, the idea of using bugs to get rid of waste is nothing new. Compost heaps use microorganisms to digest anything from potato peelings to grass cuttings. The product is nutrient-rich compost. Bioremediation takes this idea a step further, using microorganisms to convert poisonous waste into safer substances. The first large-scale test of bioremediation happened in 1989, when it was used on a patch of beach polluted with petroleum from the wrecked supertanker *Exxon Valdez*. Petroleum is a natural product that is full of energy. For those microorganisms that can digest it, it is similar to a high-fat diet. Bioremediation works by spraying the polluted area with nutrients and tilling the sand or soil to provide oxygen. Microorganisms that are already in the ground then have a diet on which they can thrive. Their numbers grow as they use oxygen to metabolize the petroleum, producing smaller, simpler molecules that cause less environmental damage.

Many of the organic compounds in industrial waste also form in nature, so it is not surprising that there is usually a microorganism somewhere in nature that has an appetite for most types of waste. When bioremediation is used to treat waste water and gases from factories, the population of microorganisms gradually adjusts to suit the cocktail of waste products.

Some of the most dangerous pollutants are chlorinated (containing chlorine) compounds that do not appear in nature at all. Dioxins, PCBs (polychlorinated biphenyls), and some pesticides belong to this group. Even so, scientists have managed to find natural bacteria that will digest a wood preservative and a herbicide that contains chlorine. Some scientists believe microorganisms could be genetically engineered (bred in special laboratories) to deal with other chlorinated wastes.

Bioremediation does not work for all types of pollution. Inorganic wastes, such as heavy-metal compounds, resist treatment. Even small amounts of heavy metals can kill microorganisms and prevent them from treating organic wastes. When bioremediation does work, it is cheap, effective, and causes less environmental disturbance than other waste-disposal techniques such as incineration or landfill.

The bioremediated patch at the **Exxon Valdez** *wreck showed a distinct improvement when it was compared to the nonbioremediated beach.*

In 1953 biochemist Sir Hans Krebs received (with Fritz Lipmann) the Nobel Prize for physiology or medicine, for the discovery of the citric acid cycle (also called the Krebs cycle).

Enzymes

Enzymes are proteins that work as biochemical catalysts (molecules that speed up or slow down particular chemical reactions). They are remarkably effective, causing reactions in the body that would often require much higher temperatures and pressures if the equivalent industrial catalysts were used. Enzymes bring together molecules in a position that causes them to react. After a catalytic group in the enzyme causes the reaction, the products of the reaction free themselves from the enzyme, which itself ends up exactly the same after as before the reaction. The three-dimensional shape of an enzyme is critical for it to be able to hold reacting molecules and then release products. Biochemists often compare this fit to that of a key in a lock.

The first enzyme to be separated from a natural source and then purified was urease (YOOR-ee-ayz), a protein in the jack bean that converts urea and water into carbon dioxide and ammonia. The separation of urease was first done in 1926 by U.S. biochemist James Sumner (1887–1955). Sumner used the crystals of pure urease to study, in the laboratory, a reaction that would normally happen in a living organism. Since then, biochemists have studied a number of purified enzymes. All have proved to be proteins. In some cases, natural proteins have been modified to make them resistant to heat, bleach, and alkaline conditions; others have been modified to boost their efficiency. The grease-digesting agents in biological washing powders are types of enzymes.

The citric acid cycle

The citric acid cycle is a sequence of reactions showing how sugars and fats are metabolized (converted) to produce energy for living organisms plus carbon dioxide and water. A number of enzymes take part in the reactions of the cycle. The product of the cycle that carries chemical energy in a form cells can use is called adenosine triphosphate (ATP). The cycle was first suggested by German-born British biochemist Sir Hans Krebs (1900–1981).

DNA and genetics

DNA (deoxyribonucleic acid) is the instruction kit with which an organism makes its proteins. DNA consists of two molecular strands that twist around one another in a double helix. The backbone of each strand is a chain of molecules containing phosphorus and ribose, a type of sugar. Other molecules, called bases, are attached along the chain. There are four bases: adenine, cytosine, guanine, and thymine. The names of the bases are abbreviated to A, C, G, and T. The bases stick out from the chains like the teeth of a zipper. There is an important difference from a zipper, though, because the bases in the two strands pair up rather than mesh together. A always pairs with T, and C always pairs with G, so a sequence ACGT in one strand is matched by a sequence TGCA in the other.

The structure of DNA

The search for the structure of DNA started in 1951 at King's College, London, when British chemist Rosalind Franklin (1920–1958) began to study DNA using X-ray diffraction. In X-ray diffraction, the pattern of dots formed when X rays bounce off a crystal onto a photographic plate gives information about the crystal's structure. In straightforward crystals, such as the crystals of sodium chloride (NaCl), molecules or ions form a very simple pattern that repeats in three dimensions. Their X-ray diffraction patterns are straightforward and clear. Complex molecules, such as DNA, produce more blurred patterns. Franklin used a fine X-ray beam when studying strands of DNA. By doing this, she

Rosalind Franklin's work played an important part in the discovery of the structure of DNA.

STORY OF SCIENCE

The Stuff of Life

In 1953, U.S. chemists Harold Urey (1893–1981) and Stanley Miller (born 1930) set about a series of experiments that must have resembled scenes from the horror movies of that era. Wondering how life had started on Earth, they filled flasks with mixtures of ammonia, hydrogen, methane, and water vapor, placed two electrodes in each flask, and sent a high-voltage spark through the mixtures. After a few days of continuous sparks, they opened the flasks to test what they had made.

In their experiment, Urey and Miller had re-created what scientists believe was the atmosphere of Earth when life started to form. The sparks were to reproduce lightning flashes, which would have been frequent in such an atmosphere and could have provided the energy for chemical changes. When they tested the contents of the flask, they found that the mixtures they had produced contained amino acids and other compounds that are the building blocks of proteins and other materials essential to life.

Other experimenters have since made similar mixtures using ultraviolet light and heat as energy sources instead of the artificial lightning of the original experiments.

limited the amount of blurring in the diffraction pattern. She found that the X-ray pattern depended on whether the sample was wet or dry. She called the dry form "A" and the wet form "B." The X-ray pattern for the wet form was a cross, indicating a helical (coil) structure. Scientists were already aware that DNA consisted of chains of phosphate groups, sugar groups, and bases, but they did not know how they were joined together. Observing that water could become attached to the coiled DNA, Franklin reasoned that the phosphate groups, which attract water most, must be on the outside of the coil.

In May 1952, Franklin obtained an X-ray pattern of the B form that was clear enough for her to calculate that DNA is a double helix (two intertwined spiral strands). She was still uncertain about how the two strands held together, and it was not until March 1953 that she worked out that the two strands were held together by bonds between pairs of bases. Unfortunately for Franklin, British biochemist Francis Crick (born 1916) and U.S. biochemist James Watson (born 1928) published their proposed structure for DNA on March 18, 1953. Crick and Watson had started to work on theories of the structure after seeing some of Franklin's early results. Crick and Watson won the 1962 Nobel Prize in physiology or medicine for explaining the structure of DNA. Franklin would have shared it with them, but she had died four years before.

Protein formation

DNA splits into its two strands to help form proteins. One strand carries the recipes for proteins in its base sequence. A unique string of three bases, called a codon, provides the instructions for each amino acid. CAG provides the instructions for the amino acid valine. A string of 300 bases might line up 100 amino acids in the correct order to make a protein, though this happens with the help of shorter DNA-like molecules called RNA (ribonucleic acid).

A gene is a sequence within the strand of DNA that codes for the sequence of a protein. Enzymes called restriction nucleases are used by scientists to cut the DNA strand and insert new genes. This is genetic engineering. Genetic engineers can add genes from one type of living thing to the DNA of another, or they change the base sequence of a gene to make a new type of protein. This is how plants such as soybeans have been made to resist certain pests, and tomatoes have been made to remain firm for longer. These are examples of genetically modified (GM) foods. However, some people are worried that the added genes will be spread to wild plants. Wild plants with these extra genes could result in many other natural species being wiped out. Other scientists are concerned that the system used to add genes is unsafe and that the genes could transfer themselves to other living organisms or become viruses.

Scientists are experimenting with ways to help cure people who have inherited diseases. Such diseases are passed down from earlier generations through faulty genes. Cystic fibrosis, muscular dystrophy, and a type of diabetes are examples of such diseases. One curing technique could be to use a genetically modified virus to change the faulty DNA of a patient. Similar techniques might also help build the resistance of cells to the human immunodeficiency virus (HIV), which causes acquired immune deficiency syndrome (AIDS).

CHECK THESE OUT!
✔CHEMISTRY ✔PROTEIN ✔SPECTROSCOPY

A scientist pollinates a wheat flower. Plant breeding is an important stage in producing GM crops.

Biosphere

The part of Earth where life is possible, including parts of the land, water, and air

The part of Earth that contains life is called the biosphere. It forms a layer around the planet that includes the atmosphere, seas, land surface, and the ground to a certain depth. The vertical range of the biosphere is huge, from high in the atmosphere down to the bottom of the deep oceans and underground. Bacteria (single-celled organisms) and birds have been found above 25,000 feet (7,500 m) and they can live up to 8 miles (13 km) underground. However, most life on Earth exists in a relatively narrow band that stretches from a little below sea level to a height of 3,280 feet (1,000 m). Far fewer living things exist near the limits of the biosphere, at great heights or depths.

Earth's atmosphere forms the upper level of the biosphere. It traps energy from the Sun and regulates temperatures on Earth. It also reflects part of the Sun's rays and filters out harmful radiation, such as cosmic rays and ultraviolet light, and so plays a vital role in sustaining life. The outer layer of Earth is called the crust. Below a certain depth, temperatures are too hot and the pressure is too great for life to exist.

Biomes

A biome is a large region with a particular type of vegetation. Various parts of the globe form different biomes, where conditions depend on factors such as the region's geography, its climate, and the distance from the equator (ih-KWAY-tuhr; an imaginary circle around Earth at equal distances from the North and South Poles). Earth's main biomes include the deserts, forests, grasslands, and mountains in tropical, temperate, and polar regions.

About 70 percent of Earth's surface is covered by water. Of the dry land, about a third is desert, and a further 20 percent is covered by either ice or tundra (the barren, treeless lowlands of the far north). So even within the biosphere, large areas of Earth support a relatively small number of living things, which are well adapted to survive there. In contrast, areas with more favorable climates, including forests, grasslands, and

shallow seas in the tropics, support huge numbers of living organisms.

Chemical cycles

Living organisms are made up of water, carbon, hydrogen, oxygen, nitrogen, and phosphorus. All these chemicals are continually recycled between the living and the nonliving world.

All energy on Earth comes from the sunlight captured by plants and algae (AL-jee; plantlike organisms) through the photosynthetic process. This changes water, minerals, and carbon dioxide from the air into food for plants and algae. Oxygen is produced as a waste product, and it is used by most organisms to fuel their body

processes. Body processes return carbon dioxide to the atmosphere, maintaining the cycle.

Earth in balance

For millions of years, Earth has regulated and maintained itself. Living organisms live and grow using chemicals from their food, but they return the same chemicals to the nonliving world in their waste products and when they die.

Living organisms have evolved (developed) to depend on one another in a web of life. Plants and algae produce their food using energy from sunlight. Animals feed on plants or algae, or prey upon one another. Some living organisms, including fungi and bacteria, help to recycle chemicals back to the nonliving world by consuming and breaking down waste products and dead bodies.

The natural world is able to recover from disaster. Various cycles act as buffers against sudden changes such as volcanic eruptions, which can cause great devastation, depositing ash or lava over a wide area. In a few years, plants begin to sprout again in the lava or ash (which contains important trace elements). Fire is part of the natural cycle in grasslands and forests. Living organisms are adapted to cope with it.

The biosphere's delicate balance must be maintained not only for the sake of humankind, but also for the future of the whole of planet Earth.

Nature unbalanced

Human activities threaten to upset the natural balance of the biosphere. Industries and agriculture produce poisonous by-products that pollute the air, water, and land.

Chemical fertilizers from farming run off into streams and rivers, harming water creatures. When large oil tankers accidentally spill their cargoes of crude oil, it causes widespread damage to marine life.

The burning of fossil fuels produces acid rain, which harms trees and other plants. This process also increases the proportion of gases such as carbon dioxide in the atmosphere, which has a general warming effect on Earth's climate. The buildup of chemicals called chlorofluorocarbons (CFCs) in the atmosphere has partly destroyed the ozone layer, which shields Earth from ultraviolet light.

In the past, humans lived in ways that worked with nature rather than against it. More recently, modern societies have tended to exploit the natural world without care for the future. Now people are becoming more aware of the delicate balance of the biosphere.

CHECK THESE OUT!
✔DESERT ✔EARTH ✔FOREST ✔GLOBAL WARMING
✔GRASSLAND ✔MOUNTAIN ✔POLAR REGION
✔POLLUTION ✔TEMPERATE REGION
✔TROPICAL REGION ✔TUNDRA ✔WATER ✔WETLAND

Black Hole

An area of space with gravity so strong that no matter or light can escape from it

A black hole is the entire mass of a huge star pulled in by its own gravity (the force of attraction between all objects in the Universe) to a tiny point in space. It is the densest object in the Universe. A black hole's gravity is so strong that even light, the fastest thing in the Universe, cannot escape from it. This makes black holes invisible, but astronomers can detect them by their effects on the matter surrounding them.

How black holes form

Black holes are created when the biggest stars in the Universe die. All stars generate energy from nuclear reactions in their cores. The pressure of this energy rushing out through the star, in the form of light, holds up the star's outer layers against the pull of gravity from the core. Stars do not shine forever, though, and when the nuclear fuel in the core is exhausted and the outward pressure of light disappears, gravity takes over.

In the case of a star like the Sun, this is quite a gentle process. The star puffs off its outer layers, and the core slowly collapses on itself until the atoms inside it are tightly packed together. The star has become a white dwarf, about the size of Earth, with a density of roughly 400 pounds/cubic inch (100 kg/cubic cm).

When a much larger star (one that is at least eight times heavier than the Sun) comes to an end, the process is much more violent. The star blasts off most of its mass in a huge explosion called a supernova, and for a short time it can outshine an entire galaxy. The remaining core of

A black hole at the center of this huge galaxy (called Centaurus A; the nearest galaxy to our own) is believed to be sucking in stars from a smaller galaxy that has collided with Centaurus A.

the star, still several times the mass of the Sun, then falls back under its own gravity, with such speed and violence that the atoms inside it are broken apart. The compression usually stops when the neutrons (uncharged particles) from their atomic nuclei (centers) are tightly packed together. The resulting neutron star has a width of just a few miles.

Black holes are created when the star's collapse does not stop at the neutron star stage. This only happens when the collapsing core of the star is at

HIGHLIGHTS

♦ Black holes are areas of space where the force of gravity is so strong that even light, the fastest thing in the Universe, cannot escape.

♦ So much mass in such a small space makes space and time around black holes behave differently from ordinary space and time.

least three times heavier than our Sun. Its gravity is then strong enough to squeeze the neutrons together with no stopping. The core pulls in on itself until it becomes so dense that the gravity around it will not even allow light to escape. It has sealed itself off completely from the outside Universe and has become a black hole.

Inside a black hole

To anyone looking from the outside, a black hole would appear to be a completely black sphere in space. This sphere, called the event horizon, marks the point where the collapsed star's gravity becomes strong enough to stop light from escaping. The event horizon is not a physical object. It is a point of no return. The star inside has collapsed to a point of infinite density and no volume, called a singularity.

Singularities have very strong effects on the space around them. As the black hole pulls in nearby material, it also warps space and slows down time around it. With a spinning black hole, the event horizon is surrounded by a whirlpool-like region of space called an ergosphere, and the singularity inside is ring-shaped. Some astronomers think that a spinning black hole could distort space so much that it punches a wormhole through to another part of the Universe—but it would be too unstable for anything to travel through it.

Finding black holes

Because they do not give out any light, black holes floating in space are difficult to detect. All the known black holes have been found because of the way they affect material around them. The first black hole candidate was discovered when astronomers detected X rays coming from the space close to a star in the constellation Cygnus (the Swan). Astronomers think this source, called Cygnus X-1, is a black hole in orbit with another star (a binary system). The two stars formed at the same time, but the larger one became a black hole while the smaller one was still a normal star.

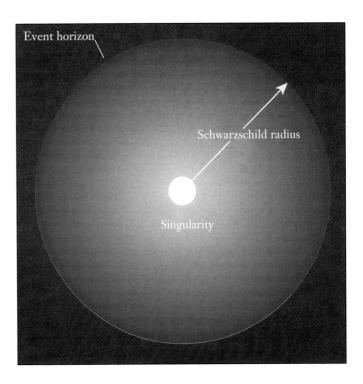

A nonrotating black hole has a singularity and an event horizon. The distance between the two parts is called the Schwarzschild radius.

Now the black hole's enormous gravity is pulling material off its companion. As this material spirals down into the black hole, it is heated up and torn apart, giving off X rays in the process.

Astronomers think giant black holes lie at the center of many galaxies. It is possible that these black holes were formed at the beginning of the Universe when conditions were violent. During the 1960s, astronomers discovered quasars (KWAY-zahrz), objects that looked like stars but were actually billions of light years away. To be visible over this distance, quasars had to be millions of times brighter than normal galaxies, yet they sometimes changed their brightness very quickly. The best theory to explain quasars is that they are young galaxies with giant black holes at their centers. The black hole has collected a disk of matter around it, which is being heated up as it falls into the hole, and gives off brilliant light. Some astronomers think that Earth's own Milky Way and galaxies like it could have sleeping black holes in their centers.

CHECK THESE OUT!
✔GALAXY ✔GRAVITY ✔SPACE ✔STAR ✔UNIVERSE

Calcium

The fifth most abundant element in Earth's crust and oceans is calcium, which occurs mainly as different forms of the compound calcium carbonate ($CaCO_3$). Limestone, marble, chalk, coral, seashells, and eggshells all consist of calcium carbonate. Calcium is a soft, silver-white metal that melts at 1562°F (850°C). When heated in air, calcium forms calcium oxide (CaO). In all compounds, calcium exists as the Ca^{2+} ion. Calcium also forms simple ionic compounds when heated with fluorine, chlorine, bromine, iodine, and nitrogen. It reacts violently with water to form calcium hydroxide and hydrogen.

Extracting calcium

As with other reactive metals, the only means of extracting calcium from its compounds is by the process of electrolysis (the use of an electrical current to cause a chemical change in a compound). British chemist Sir Humphry Davy (1778–1829) first extracted calcium by passing an electrical current though a mixture of calcium oxide and mercury. The electrolysis produced a mixture of calcium and mercury, and Davy boiled off the mercury to obtain pure calcium. Today, calcium is obtained by electrolyzing molten calcium chloride ($CaCl_2$).

Calcium minerals

Limestone, marble, and chalk are forms of calcium carbonate that differ because of how they are formed. Marble is calcium carbonate that melted and then crystallized slowly. When limestone is powdered and baked, it gives off carbon dioxide and becomes calcium oxide (CaO), also called quicklime. Quicklime reacts fiercely with water, releasing heat as it turns into calcium hydroxide (slaked lime), which is used to make mortar and to reduce acidity in soil and water. Rock phosphate is calcium phosphate. Treated with sulfuric acid, it releases phosphoric acid and forms calcium sulfate. Rock phosphate is a useful fertilizer. Fluorite is calcium fluoride (CaF_2). It is used to make fluorine. Gypsum is calcium sulfate dihydrate ($CaSO_4.2H_2O$). Heating gypsum drives off water to produce a powder called plaster of paris. A mixture of plaster of paris and water, soaked into bandages, is used to make casts around broken limbs. Adding water re-forms gypsum, which sets around the limb. This process is now being replaced by the use of fiberglass strips, which can quickly be bonded to each other with a polymer glue.

Calcium in the body

Around 2 percent of the weight of the human body is calcium, and 99 percent of that calcium is combined in calcium hydroxyphosphate, which makes up bones and teeth. Some of the remaining calcium is needed in the nervous system. A person who eats too little calcium may get brittle bones, as they lose calcium from their skeleton. Dairy foods and leafy green vegetables are good sources of calcium.

Calcium is needed by the body in order to maintain healthy bones, as seen here under the microscope.

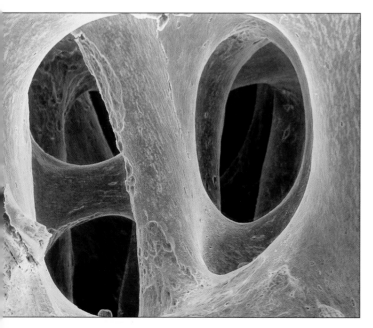

CHECK THESE OUT!
✔ACID AND BASE ✔ALLOY ✔ALUMINUM
✔BATTERY ✔CAVE ✔IGNEOUS ROCK
✔IRON AND STEEL ✔METAL ✔WATER

Glossary

acid rain Rain polluted by sulfur and nitrogen oxide emissions from burning coal and oil; damages buildings and plants.

airstream Flow of air around a flying object, such as an airplane.

analog Showing data in a continuously variable form, for example, with a moving pointer or clock hands. *See also* digital.

atom bomb Bomb with huge explosive power created by nuclear fission.

atomic number Number that determines an element's chemical properties and where it is in the periodic table. It represents the number of protons in an atom.

center of gravity Point in a three-dimensional object. If the object is supported at this point, it will balance.

colony Group of individuals of one species living together.

corrosion Process of wearing away by chemical action.

digital Representing data in the form of numbers. *See also* analog.

elliptical (ih-LIP-tih-kuhl) Oval.

flight controller Somebody who controls an airplane or spacecraft flight by signal from the ground.

gorge Narrow, V-shaped valley.

hard water Water containing calcium and magnesium ions; does not lather easily with soap.

hormone Chemicals produced in the body that have specific effects on certain cell activity.

icebreaker Ship with a strong hull to break through sea ice.

inert gases Group of rare gases that includes helium and neon; very stable and rarely react.

internal combustion engine Engine in which fuel is combusted (burned) inside the engine itself.

lichen (LY-kuhn) Organism made up of a fungus and alga.

metabolize (muh-TA-buh-LYZ) The way that cells convert a substance by chemical changes in order to use it for life processes.

mortar (MAWR-tuhr) Building material that is a mixture of cement, lime, sand, and water.

mountain building Gradual process whereby Earth's plates collide, reshaping Earth's crust.

nerve receptors Cells in the nerves that receive stimuli.

neutralize (NYOO-truh-LYZ) To make neutral, i.e. neither acidic nor alkaline.

overfishing Harvesting sea life until the stock is threatened.

pancreas (PAN-kree-uhs) Large gland in the body of back-boned animals that makes enzymes needed for digestion and the hormones insulin and glucagon.

pharmacologist (FAHR-muh-KAH-luh-jist) Chemist involved in creating new medical drugs.

phase (FAYZ) Appearance of a planet or moon from Earth.

pivot (PIH-vuht) Shaft or pin on which something turns.

salt lake Landlocked body of water that has become salty through evaporation.

shock wave Compressed wave caused by a disturbance such as an explosion or an earthquake.

short circuit Point of low resistance in a circuit that allows more power to flow. This can damage the circuit elsewhere.

toxic (TAHK-sik) Poisonous.

trace element Chemical element found in tiny quantities, for example in an ore.

transmit To send radio waves between a transmitter and a receiver.

twilight (TWY-lyt) Time between night and sunrise or between sunset and full night.

warp Distortion.

Index

Page numbers in **boldface type** refer to main articles and their illustrations. Page numbers in *italic type* refer to additional illustrations.

| 550
EXP
#1 | Exploring Earth and
Space Science | | |

05/06	**DATE DUE**